PRACTICE
PRACTICE
PRACTICE

BOOK III

BY ST² PUBLISHING
TIMOTHY A. TRINKLE
THOMAS R. FITTS
STEVEN G. SELBY

EACH PAGE CONTAINS 18 PROBLEMS:

WARMUPS
PROPORTIONS, AREA
EQUATIONS, PERCENTS
WORD PROBLEMS

WHOLE NUMBERS	INTEGERS
DECIMALS	PROPORTIONS
FRACTIONS	PERCENTS
TIME	TOURNAMENT
MONEY	MONEY
GRAPHS	PROBABILITY
EQUATIONS	TEST PREPARATION
MIXTURES	PROBLEM SOLVING

ABOUT THE AUTHORS

TIMOTHY A. TRINKLE - Received his BA from UCLA and Masters in Education from Portland State University. He taught mathematics in the Longview, Washington School District for 30 years. He previously taught in the Los Angeles School District. He now works with student teachers for Washington State University and helps run ST^2 Publishing.

STEVEN G. SELBY - Received his BS and Masters of Education from Oregon State University. He taught mathematics in the Longview, Washington School District for 30 years. He now teaches in the private sector and helps run ST^2 Publishing.

THOMAS R. FITTS - Received his BA from Washington State University and his Masters Degree from Lewis & Clark College. He taught mathematics in the Longview, Washington School District for 30 years. He now helps run ST^2 Publishing.

1st Printing   2004
ISBN 0-943542-05-7

ST^2 Publishing
191 Inglewood Dr.
Longview, WA 98632
Tel.   360-636-2645
Fax   360-414-5243
E-mail   st2pub@kalama.com
Web site   st2pub.com

FOREWARD

Book III of *Practice, Practice, Practice* was written, as were Books I+ and II+, to: (1) provide the classroom teacher with an abundant source of quality practice problems in addition to their regular text book; (2) provide the classroom teacher with a source of enrichment problems for those students who need a little extra practice or those who want to get ahead of the regular program; and (3) provide parents a source of problems o work individually with their children at home.

Book III was written with 18 problems on each page. The first ten problems are **warmups.** These are written to be done in 3 minutes. They use easy numbers and cover: decimals, fractions, percents, money, square root, and exponents. The **middle three** problems are easy equations, proportions, area, perimeter, etc.. These three problems are also meant to provide review for your students quickly with a variety of simple problems. The last five problems on each page are **word problems.** They cover the topics listed on the previous page plus many combination pages to help your students get ready for tests.

Proper use of *Practice, Practice, Practice* books can save the teacher time and their school district money. By using the detailed Table of Contents, the classroom teacher can produce an instant lesson plan, a review, or extra problems to augment a normal lesson plan. A **CLASSROOM SET** of *Practice, Practice, Practice* will eliminate most of the duplication expenses in your math department. Since the classroom teacher will **not** have to make up new problems and answers, send things to get printed, or look up things in a guide, the classroom set will greatly reduce the teacher's preparation time!!

This is the third book in the *Practice, Practice, Practice* series. Future books in this series are being planned and organized. If you have any questions about Book I+, Book II+, or this book, feel free to call, fax, email, or write:

ST^2 Publishing
191 Inglewood Dr.
Longview, WA 98632
Tel: 360-636-2645
Fax: 360-414-5243
E-mail: st2pub@kalama.com
Web site: st2pub.com

Thank you,
The Authors

PREFACE

Book III is set up to help teachers supplement their lessons. Each lesson (page) is set up to stand alone for a period or to be used in some part to supplement a lesson. All pages have the following sections.

WARMUPS

Problems 1-10 on each page are set up to be done in two to three minutes. These are not long problems. They are easy problems to help your students review: Whole Numbers, Decimals, Fractions, Percents, Integers, Exponents and Square Roots. If you use the warmups once or twice a week, your students will be able to keep up on these topics and not forget them.

THE MIDDLE THREE PROBLEMS

Problems 11-13 on each page are designed to refresh your students (or help them learn the first time) on: Equations, Inequalities, Proportions, Percents, Area and Perimeter. They might take a little longer than the Warmups, but still contain easy to use numbers. If you use these three problems twice a week, your students should not forget these topics.

THE WORD PROBLEMS

Problems 14-18 on each page are word problems. Some are grouped by topic, some are mixtures, some relate to state tests and some are just old fashioned word problems. They are set up to help you supplement a lesson. If you need one, three, or 15 word problems, we have them. You do not have to make up the problems and answers. Take a look in the table of contents for the types of word problems you need. We have two topics that may be new to you, Time and Tournament Word problems.

THE ANSWER BOOK

The answer book has two sections. The first section just lists the answers in order by page. The second section is the "Help and Hints" section. The problems that have an * by the answer are listed in the "Help and Hints" section. They have one method of solving the problem. Remember, there are several ways to solve most math problems and the "Help and Hints" section just gives you one way.

TABLE OF CONTENTS

PRACTICE PRACTICE PRACTICE BOOKS I+ AND II+
ARE TIME SAVERS FOR MATH TEACHERS.

    These mixtures are all different types. There are some logic, some common sense, some proportions, and some good old fashion word problems. Get to know what type of problems you have. These problems should save you hours in teacher preparation time!!!

Help and Hints Section
    The back of the answer book has a help section. If an answer has an * by it in the answer book, there are some "hints" in the Help Section. These "hints" may assist you in solving the problem. Remember, there are many ways to solve math problems. These "hints" are just one solution.

ST^2 PUBLISHING
    360-636-2645 TEL
    360-414-5243 FAX
    st2pub@kalama.com EMAIL
    st2pub.com   WEB SITE

LESSON #1 WHOLE NUMBERS

WARM UPS
1. $24.12 + $3
2. $24.12 + $3.13
3. $24.12 − $3
4. $24.12 − $3.13
5. $24 × 20
6. $24 ÷ 4
7. $24 ÷ 40
8. $24.12 × 20
9. 2^3
10. $\sqrt{9}$

SOLVE THE FOLLOWING:

11. $M + 12 = 17$
12. $M − 12 = 17$
13. $M + 17 = 12$

PROBLEM #14
Lee missed 6 problems on his first math quiz. He missed 9, 10 and 1 on his next three quizzes. How many did he miss in all?
A. 16   B. 24   C. 26   D. 31

PROBLEM #15
Shawna got 28 right on her first test. She then got 37, 48, 29, and 42 right on her next 4 tests. What was the total she got correct on her five tests?
A. 174   B. 184   C. 194   D. 142

PROBLEM #16
ST^2 Book Publishing's book sales starting this year were: in January 46 books, in February 398 books, in March 148 books, and in April 796 books. What is the sum of the books sold in the first three months of the year?
A. 402   B. 1,388   C. 613   D. 592

PROBLEM #17
ST^2 Book Publishing then sold 1022 books in May and 808 books in June. How many books did they sell in the first six months of this year?
A. 2,626   B. 4,848   C. 1,830   D. 3,218

PROBLEM #18
How many books did ST^2 sell in the even months so far this year?
A. 1,216   B. 1,992   C. 2,002   D. 1,836

(1)

LESSON #2 WHOLE NUMBERS

WARMUPS
1. $30 + $5.57
2. $30 − $5.57
3. $30.44 + $5
4. $30.44 − $5
5. $30.44 + $5.57
6. $30.44 − $5.57
7. $30 ÷ 6
8. $30.12 ÷ 6
9. 3^2
10. $\sqrt{16}$

SOLVE THE FOLLOWING:
11. C + 8 = 20
12. H − 8 = 20
13. N − 20 = 8

PROBLEM #14
Mr. Chinchen has 5 classes of math this fall. He has classes of 28, 24, 23, 29, and 34 students. How many total students does Mr. Chinchen have this fall?
    A. 94   B. 146   C. 128   D. 138

PROBLEM #15
What is the difference between Mr. Chinchen's largest and smallest classes?
    A. 10   B. 11   C. 57   D. 5

PROBLEM #16
In Mr. Chinchen's school the average class size is 28. How many classes of Mr. Chinchen's are over this average?
    A. 0   B. 2   C. 3   D. 5

PROBLEM #17
Mr. Chinchen's school has 987 students. Last year it had 879 students. How many more students does it have this year?
    A. 92   B. 98   C. 1,866   D. 108

PROBLEM #18   How many students in Mr. Chinchen's school don't have him for a math teacher this year?
    A. 859   B. 749   C. 849   D. 841

LESSON #3 WHOLE NUMBERS

WARMUPS
1. $21 + $79
2. $21.50 + $79
3. $21 + $79.44
4. $21.50 + $79.44
5. $79.44 − $21
6. $79 − $21.50
7. $79 − 21
8. $21.50
   ×   20
9. 4^2
10. $\sqrt{25}$

SOLVE THE FOLLOWING:
11. $F + 8 = 40$
12. $8F = 40$
13. $F − 8 = 40$

Mr. Fitts' grading scale in his math class is based on 500 points.
It is as follows: A.   450 - 500
                   B.   400 - 449
                   C.   325 - 399
                   D.   250 - 324
                   F.   0 - 249

PROBLEM #14
Joe's test scores were 94, 83, 62, 58 and 75. What would his grade be?
   a. A   b. C   c. D   d. F

PROBLEM #15
Mary's test scores were 28, 96, 97, 83, and 98. What would her grade be?
   a. A   b. B   c. C   d. D

PROBLEM #16
Julio had a 73, an 84, a 63 and a 78 on his first four tests. What would he need to get on his last test to get a B?
   a. 82   b. 92   c. 102   d. 27

PROBLEM #17
Stanley did extra credit for 28 points and had 91, 78 and 79 on his first three tests. He has two more tests to take. How many points will he need on his next two tests to get an A?
   a. 180   b. 174   c. 204   d. 154

PROBLEM #18
What is the difference in points of getting the lowest "C" and getting the lowest "A"?
   a. 125   b. 101   c. 175   d. 51

LESSON #4 WHOLE NUMBERS

WARMUPS
1. $20 − $7.52   4. $20.52 + $7.48   7. $20.50   9. 6^2
2. $20 − $.52   5. $20 + $7.52 $\times\quad 9$ 10. $\sqrt{49}$
3. $20.52 − $7   6. $20.52 + $7   8. $20.50 ÷ 5

SOLVE THE FOLLOWING:
11. T + 24 = 50
12. T − 24 = 50
13. T ÷ 4 = 6

PROBLEM #14
ST^2 Publishing packs 36 Practice Practice Practice books in each case. If they sold 12 cases, how many books did they sell?
    A. 532   B. 48   C. 432   D. 108

PROBLEM #15
Book #I has 10,000 math problems in it. If ST^2 sold 6 cases of these books, how many problems did they sell?
    A. 10,650   B. 60,000   C. 360,000   D. 2,160,000

PROBLEM #16
Book #II has 213 pages in it. All but 50 pages have 50 problems on a page. These 50 pages have a total of 1,126 problems. How many problems are in Book II?
    A. 10,650   B. 8,150   C. 9,276   D. 10,126

PROBLEM #17
One month, ST^2 sold 15 cases of books. Six cases were sent back. How many books did they end up selling that month?
    A. 324   B. 1,980   C. 2,196   D. 2088

PROBLEM #18
In a three month span; ST^2 sold 16 cases, 14 cases and 25 cases of books. How many books did they sell in those 3 months?
    A. 108   B. 1,980   C. 2,196   D. 2,088

(4)

LESSON #5   WHOLE NUMBERS

WARMUPS

1. $25 – $13.47   4. $25 – $.13   7. $25.80   9. 5^2
2. $25.47 – $13   5. $25 – $1.30 $\underline{\times \quad 40}$ 10. $\sqrt{100}$
3. $25.30 – $13.47   6. $25 + $5.44 + $1.56   8. $25.80 ÷ 5

SOLVE THE FOLLOWING:

11. $N + 17 = 30$
12. $N – 17 = 30$
13. $30 ÷ N = 5$

PROBLEM #14

Mr. Heinz likes to read books. During a two week period he read 5 books. They had 218 pages, 306 pages, 423 pages, 185 pages, and 276 pages. How many total pages did Mr. Heinz read during the two week period?

A. 1,418   B. 1,413   C. 1,408   D. 1,415

PROBLEM #15

If Mr. Heinz kept up the same pace of 5 books every two weeks, how many books would he read in a year?

A. 260   B. 31   C. 250   D. 130

PROBLEM #16

One week, Mr. Heinz read two books of 276 pages each. The next week he read a book of 185 pages. How many more pages did he read in the first week?

A. 91   B. 737   C. 367   D. 461

PROBLEM #17

During October, Mr. Heinz averaged reading 53 pages a day. How many total pages did he read in October?

A. 1,590   B. 84   C. 636   D. 1,643

PROBLEM #18

Mr. Heinz had a goal of reading 100 books last year. He only read 96. If each book averaged 214 pages, how many pages did Mr. Heinz read last year?

A. 21,400   B. 41,944   C. 20,544   D. 856

(5)

LESSON #6   WHOLE NUMBERS

WARMUPS
1. $35 – $27.62
2. $35.62 – $27
3. $35 – $14
4. $35 – $1.40
5. $35 – $.14

6. $35.50
   $\times$ 8

7. $35.50
   $\times$ 800

8. $35.50 $\div$ 5
9. 5^3
10. $\sqrt{100}$

SOLVE THE FOLLOWING:
11. $10B = 40$
12. $40 \div B = 4$
13. $B + 10 = 40$

PROBLEM #14
A new movie theatre in Baytown has 23 rows of seats. Each row has 16 seats. How many seats are in the theatre?
   A. 39   B. 288   C. 388   D. 368

PROBLEM #15
At one showing of a movie there were 257 people watching the movie. If 142 of these people were male, how many were female?
   A. 115   B. 399   C. 205   D. 95

PROBLEM #16
Another movie had 123 male and 145 female customers. If 48 of these customers were children, how many adults were there?
   A. 316   B. 220   C. 36   D. 268

PROBLEM #17
The same theatre showed a movie 4 times a day for 7 days. The average attendance for each showing was 78. How many total people watched the movie that week?
   A. 546   B. 136   C. 858   D. 2,184

PROBLEM #18
If this same theatre in Baytown showed three new movies every week, how many new movies would they show in a year?
   A. 156   B. 300   C. 52   D. 17

(6)

LESSON #7   WHOLE NUMBERS

WARMUPS

1. $12.3 - 4$
2. $12.3 - 40$
3. $12.3 - .4$

4. $12.3 + 4.04$
5. $12.3 \div 6$
6. $12.3 \div .006$

7. $\begin{array}{r} \$25.45 \\ \times \quad .04 \\ \hline \end{array}$
8. $\frac{3}{4} \times \$24$

9. 4^3
10. $\sqrt{36}$

SOLVE THE FOLLOWING

11. $8 / 5 = T / 10$
12. $2T + 12 = 18$
13. $T + 7.3 = 12$

PROBLEM #14
Sandy and Jill play basketball. One game, Sandy scored 28 points and Jill scored 17. How many points did they score together?
A. 44   B. 45   C. 11   D. 35

PROBLEM #15
In another game, Jill had six 3 point goals and four 2 point goals. She made no free throws for 1 point. How many points did she score?
A. 26   B. 36   C. 20   D. 30

PROBLEM #16
One game, their team lost 66 to 54. How many more 3 pointers had they needed to win the game?
A. 4   B. 5   C. 6   D. 12

PROBLEM #17
One day, a bakery sold 1,296 donuts. How many dozen is this?
A. 116   B. 36   C. 108   D. 18

PROBLEM #18
The bakery had a slow day and only sold 12 dozen donuts. They had 48 customers that they sold to. On an average, how many donuts did each customer buy?
A. 4   B. 3   C. 5   D. 36

Need more quality problems, try Book I+ and Book II+.
ST² PUBLISHING -   st2pub.com
360-636-2645

WARMUPS

1. $36.37 - 5$ 4. $36.37 + 5.5$ 7. $\frac{2}{3} \times \$18$ 9. 10^5
2. $36.37 - .5$ 5. $\$36 \div 40$ 8. $\$60.60$ 10. $\sqrt{100}$
3. $36.37 - 50$ 6. $\$36 \div .004$ $\underline{\times \quad .07}$

SOLVE THE FOLLOWING

11. $15 / 20 = M / 100$
12. $8 / M = 40 / 100$
13. $3M + \$2 = \$20$

The Mustangs, a boys basketball team, scored 72 points in a game against the Huskies. There were 8 players who scored in the game. John scored 20 points, Josh 18, Kevin 4, Kareem 6, Sam 3, Vitaly 2, and Sean 2.

PROBLEM #14

If Jose was the other scorer, how many points did he score?
A. 26   B. 16   C. 17   D. 19

PROBLEM #15

What was the average points scored for these eight players in the game?
A. 7   B. 9   C. 8   D. 19

PROBLEM #16

In the above game, the Huskies had six players who averaged 9 points each. Who won the game and by how many points?
A. Huskies by 18 points.   B. Mustangs by 18 points.
C. Mustangs by 15 points.   D. Mustangs by 12 points.

PROBLEM #17

If the Mustangs had eight players who each averaged 10 points for all their games, about how many points should the Mustangs score for a game?
A. 80   B. 62   C. 88   D. 72

PROBLEM #18

If John's average for the four games before the Huskies game was 15, what would his new average be after the Huskies game?
A. 18   B. 16   C. 19   D. 22

LESSON #9   WHOLE NUMBERS + MONEY

WARMUPS

1. 24.1 − 30	4. 24.1 + 3.33	7. ¾ × $60	9. 5^3
2. 24.1 − 3	5. $60 ÷ .004	8. $60.66	10. $\sqrt{144}$
3. 24.1 − .3	6. $60.66 − $7	$\underline{\times\ \ \ .09}$	

SOLVE THE FOLLOWING:

11. $N + 34 = 51$
12. $6 / N = 9 / 15$
13. What is the perimeter and area of a square that is 7 inches on a side?

PROBLEM #14

The attendance last year for the Ephrata Tigers' five home football games was 252, 415, 368, 405, and 355. What was their total home attendance for the season?
  A. 1,795   B. 1,645   C. 1,695   D. 1,805

PROBLEM #15

What was the average attendance at the Tigers' home football games last year?
  A. 405   B. 254   C. 364   D. 359

PROBLEM #16

What was the difference between the highest and lowest game attendance?
  A. 163   B. 677   C. 153   D. 657

PROBLEM #17

If the Ephrata High School Tigers had a goal of 400 people per game, how many people did they miss their goal by?
  A. 51   B. 148   C. 41   D. They reached their goal.

PROBLEM #18

Adult admission was $1.75 and student admission cost $.75. At Ephrata's first game last year there were 91 adults and 161 students. How much money did Ephrata take in at their first football game?
  A. $327.50   B. $280.00   C. $630.00   D. $40.50

WARMUPS

1. $60 – $7.51	4. $60 – $75.21	7. $60 ÷ 15	9. 9^2
2. $60.51 – $7	5. $60.55 + $7 + $22.45	8. $60.51	10. $\sqrt{64}$
3. $60 – $.72	6. $60 ÷ 6	$\underline{\times\quad 8}$	

SOLVE THE FOLLOWING:

11. 20 / B= 12 / 15   **12. B** + 30 = 75   **13. B** + 75 = 30

In baseball, to figure out how many games a team is behind the 1st place team one must first subtract the number of wins of each team. Then the number of losses must be subtracted. The two differences are then added together and divided by two.

The current standings are:	Wins	Losses
SEATTLE	**62**	**21**
OAKLAND	**60**	**22**
CALIFORNIA	**48**	**35**
TEXAS	**40**	**41**

PROBLEM #14
How many games is California behind Seattle?
  A. 28   B. 13½   C. 14   D. 14½

PROBLEM #15
How many games is Oakland behind Seattle?
  A. 2½   B. 1½   C. 1   D. 3

PROBLEM #16
How many games is Texas behind Seattle?
  A. 20½   B. 11   C. 21   D. 22

PROBLEM #17
If Seattle lost 2 games and Oakland won 3 games, how many games would Oakland be ahead of Seattle?
  A. 1   B. They would still be behind   C. ½   D. 3

PROBLEM #18
If Texas lost 4 games and Oakland won 2 games, how many games would Texas be behind Oakland?
  A. 11½   B. 22½   C. 23   D. 45

LESSON #11   DECIMALS

WARMUPS
1. $51.27 – $8
2. $51.27 – $80
3. $51.27 – $.80
4. 40 ÷ .008
5. .008 ÷ 40
6. 7 – 5½
7. $52.25
   x   .08
8. 4.2 + 3.78 + 5
9. 2^4
10. $\sqrt{100}$

SOLVE THE FOLLOWING:
11. 8 / T = 20 / 45   **12.** .05 / 6 = I / 15   **13.**   20 / .6 = .4 / M

PROBLEM #14
It rains a lot in Longview. On three different days it rained .4 inches, .68 inches, and 1.6 inches. What is the total rainfall of those three days?
A. 5.68 in.   B. 2.68 in.   C. 1.08 in.   D. 4.352 in.

PROBLEM #15
One week it rained a total of 6.2 inches. The next week it rained 8.32 inches. How much more did it rain the second week?
A. 2.88 in.   B. 14.52 in.   C. 5.6576 in.   D. 2.12 in.

PROBLEM #16
After the two weeks in problem fifteen it rained .453 of an inch the next week. How much did it rain in the 3 week period?
A. 5.453 in   B. 19.973 in.   C. 14.973 in.   D. 2.573 in.

PROBLEM #17
If it rained 1.01 inches, but .018 inches of it evaporated, how much would be left?
A. 1.028 in.   B. 1.818 in.   C. .992 in.   D. 1.108 in.

PROBLEM #18
One report said that it rained 3 inches in two days. It actually rained 1.05 inches and 1.8 inches. How far off was the report?
A. 7.85 in.   B. .15 in.   C. 2.85 in.   D. 5.85 in.

LESSON #12   DECIMALS

WARMUPS
1. 44.2 − 9   4. ⅔ ÷ ¾   7. 9 − 3⅓   9. √400̄
2. 44.2 − .9   5. .002 ÷ 40   8. $40.70   10. 6³
3. 44.2 − 90   6. 40 ÷ .002   ×   .007

SOLVE THE FOLLOWING:
11. $8T = 5T − .24$ **12.** $30 / 24 = T / 16$ **13.** What is the area and perimeter of a square with sides of 12 cm?

PROBLEM #14
A slug crawled 1.14 m on Monday. Tuesday it crawled .96 m. How far did it crawl on the two days?
   A. 10.74 m   B. 10.844 m   C. 2.1 m   D. .18 m

PROBLEM #15
On Wednesday it crawled 2.1 m, on Thursday it crawled 1.614 m, but on Friday it ran into some salt and only crawled .24 m. How far did it crawl during this three day period?
   A. 3.954 m   B. 3.714 m   C. 1.659 m   D. 4.194 m

PROBLEM #16
How much farther did it crawl on Thursday than Friday?
   A. .625 m   B. 1.834 m   C. 1.59 m   D. 1.374 m

PROBLEM #17
The next week the slug crawled about 2.3 m each day. How far did it crawl during this seven day period?
   A. 1.61 m   B. 16.1 m   C. 11.5 m   D. 14.21 m

PROBLEM #18
Two slugs each crawled 1.11 m on a Friday. Two other slugs crawled 1.68 m and 2.4 m on that same day. How far did the four slugs crawl in all?
   A. 5.25 m   B. 4.44 m   C. 6.3 m   D. 4.14 m

(12)

LESSON #13 DECIMALS

WARMUPS
1. $3.24 - 5$ 4. $.05 \div 40$ 7. $\$51.23$ 8. $12 - 7\ 5/8$
2. $3.24 - 50$ 5. $40 \div .05$ $\underline{\times\quad .06}$ 9. 2^5
3. $3.24 - .5$ 6. $\$7.25 + \$5 + \$3.13$ 10. $\sqrt{49}$

SOLVE THE FOLLOWING:
11. $6 / T = 8 / 12$ 12. $.4T - 10 = 10$ 13. What is the area
and perimeter of a rectangle 6 cm by 9 cm?

PROBLEM #14
Jon was measuring a side for bottom side of a metal box he was making.
The side was supposed to be 14.5 cm. He measured it wrong. He was
.08 cm short. How long was the side he measured?
   A. 14.58 cm.   B. 14.52 cm   C. 13.7 cm.   D. 14.42 cm

PROBLEM #15
Jon next measured a piece of metal for the side that was the
length. He wanted it to be 20.3 cm. Again he measured wrong
and cut a piece 1.83 cm too long. How long was this piece he cut?
   A. 38.6 cm   B. 22.13 cm   C. 21.86 cm   D. 18.47 cm

PROBLEM #16
The box Jon was making, from the previous two problems,
was a rectangular box. If he had measured correctly, what would
be the perimeter of the box he intended to make?
   A. 69.6 cm   B. 34.8 cm   C. 58 cm   D. 81.2 cm

PROBLEM #17
Jon wanted to make four smaller boxes whose dimensions
would be 8.45 cm by 12.25 cm and 5 cm high. He had a sheet of
metal 5cm by 200cm. To make the sides of these boxes, how
much of this sheet of metal would he need?
   A. 165.6 cm^2 B. 33.8 cm   C. 24.70 cm   D. 82.80 cm

PROBLEM #18
Jon had another sheet of metal he was using to make the bottoms
of the four boxes in Problem #17. How many square centimeters of
metal would Jon need to make the bottoms of the 4 boxes in
Problem #17?
   A. 165.6 cm^2 B. 41,405 cm^2 C. 16,560 cm^2 D. 414.05 cm^2

LESSON #14 DECIMALS

WARMUPS
1. $33.3 - 60$ 4. $\$20 - \$5.89$ 7. $\$55.41$ 9. $(.02)^3$
2. $33.3 - 6$ 5. $\$20 \div .004$ $\underline{\times \quad .08}$ 10. $\sqrt{121}$
3. $33.3 - .6$ 6. $.005 \div 20$ 8. $8 - 5\frac{2}{3}$

SOLVE THE FOLLOWING:

11. $20 / 12 = \mathbf{T} / 15$

12. $24 / \mathbf{I} = 30 / 35$

13. $.04 / \mathbf{M} = 25 / 100$

PROBLEM #14
What is the quotient of .8 and .05?
     A. 16   B. 1.6   C. 0.0625   D. 0.85

PROBLEM #15
The difference of 1.08 and .916 is what?
     A. 0.98928   B. 1.996   C. 0.176   D. 0.164

PROBLEM #16
What is the sum of 8.8, .08, 8, and .008?
     A. 16.888   B. 9.688   C. 0.112   D. 0.712

PROBLEM #17
What is the product of .3, 2.4, and .05?
     A. 2.75   B. 0.55   C. 0.0036   D. 0.036

PROBLEM #18
What is the difference of the product of .06 and 5 and the quotient of .06 and 5?
     A. 0.312   B. 0   C. 0.288   D. 5.048

Try Practice Practice Practice Book I+ or Book II+.

ST^2 PUBLISHING
360-636-2645
st2pub@kalama.com
web.   st2pub.com

LESSON #15 DECIMALS

WARMUPS
1. $19.57 - 30$ 4. $.025 \div 5$ 7. $\begin{array}{r} \$61.16 \\ \times \quad .8 \\ \hline \end{array}$ 9. $(.03)^2$
2. $19.57 - 3$ 5. $5 \div .025$
3. $19.57 - .3$ 6. $3\frac{1}{3} \times 9$ 8. 50% of $5.00   10. $\sqrt{.0016}$

SOLVE THE FOLLOWING:
11. $W + \$7.89 = \$20.00$
12. $S - \$5.77 = \$6.23$
13. $4U - \$4.50 = \$25.50$

To find the batting average for a baseball player one divides the number of hits by the number of at bats, not counting walks or sacrifices. The result is rounded to the nearest thousandth.

PROBLEM #14
Lennie from Kelso was up five times during a game and he got 3 hits. What was his batting average for the game?

   A. .600   B. .400   C. .120   D. .060

PROBLEM #15
Kami from Toutle was up five times during a game and had two hits and two walks. What was her batting average for the game?

   A. .800   B. .333   C. .667   D. 1.5

PROBLEM #16
Kelly from Bogieville was up 11 times during the Red Devils three game series with Big Basin CC. He had 4 hits during this series. What was his batting average?

   A. .272   B. 3.75   C. .636   D. .364

PROBLEM #17
Brock from Rainier had a .429 batting average after fourteen at bats. How many hits did he have?

   A. 8   B. 33   C. 6   D. 5

PROBLEM #18
Mike C. from Toledo has a .375 batting average after 16 at bats. How many hits would he need after his next three at bats to get his batting average over .400?

   A. 1   B. 2   C. 3   D. Mike can't get there!!

LESSON #16   DECIMALS

WARMUPS

1. 71.7 – 90   4. .002 ÷ 80   7. $75.00   9. $(.03)^3$
2. 71.7 – 9   5. ¾ × $60   × ___.6   10. $\sqrt{.09}$
3. 71.7 – .9   6. 7 – 5¼   8. .03 × .03

SOLVE THE FOLLOWING:

11. 8 / 18 = **T** / 45
12. 9**I** – 12 = 24
13. 5**M** + 5.2 = -.8

PROBLEM #14

Mick drove 280.4 miles to Paris from Austin on 12.3 gallons of gas. To the nearest tenth, what was his miles per gallon?

A. 268.1 mpg   B. 22.8 mpg
C. 24.6 mpg   D. 21.9 mpg

PROBLEM #15

It took Mick 5.5 hours to drive the 280.4 miles. What was his average speed per hour? (to the nearest tenth)

A. 51.0 mph   B. 5.9 mph
C. 59.8 mph   D. 50.9 mph

PROBLEM #16

How much gas did Mick use per hour (to the nearest tenth)?

A. 2.2 gph   B. 67.7 gph
C. 6.8 gph   D. .2 gph

PROBLEM #17

Mick drove the 280.4 miles in one day. If he drove the same amount for 12.5 days, how far would he travel?

A. 22.4 miles   B. 292.9 miles
C. 3,505 miles   D. 2,929 miles

PROBLEM #18

Mick paid an average of $1.85 per gallon of gas. How much money (to the nearest ten cents) would he pay for his 12.5 day trip?

A. $231.30   B. $284.40
C. $42.20   D. $421.80

LESSON #17   FRACTIONS

WARMUPS

1. 38.1 − 4	4. 3/4 ÷ 2/3	7. 12 1/2 + 7 3/8	9. $(1/2)^3$
2. 38.1 − .4	5. 1 1/2 × 2/3	8. $25.40	10. $\sqrt{121}$
3. 38.1 − 40	6. 20 − 5 1/4	× .08	

SOLVE THE FOLLOWING:

11. T + 7¾ = 17   **12.** ⅓T + 10 = 16   **13.** ¼ / T = 2 / 6

PROBLEM #14

Stan weighed 112¼ lbs. He wanted to wrestle at the 108 lb. level. To make sure he'd make his weight he planned on getting down to 107½ lbs. How much weight did Stan need to lose?

A. 1/2 lb.   B. 5 1/4 lbs.   C. 4 3/4 lbs.   D. 4 1/4 lbs.

PROBLEM #15

The next week Stan didn't wrestle. He made it to 107 1/8 lbs., but then gained 6 1/8 lbs. How much did he weigh then?

A. 113 5/8 lbs.   B. 115 1/5 lbs.   C. 101 3/8 lbs.   D. 113 3/8 lbs.

PROBLEM #16

At the weigh in before the next match, Stan weighed 107 1/2 lbs, John weighed 145 3/8 lbs., and Tom weighed 212 1/2 lbs. How much did they weigh all together?

A. 464 5/14 lbs.   B. 464 1/8 lbs.
C. 465 3/8 lbs.   D. 455 5/14 lbs.

PROBLEM #17

How much more did Stan and John weigh together than Tom by himself?

A. 252 7/8 lbs   B. 39 5/8 lbs   C. 67 1/8 lbs   D. 40 3/8 lbs.

PROBLEM #18

Stan wanted to wrestle at 101 lbs, John at 141 lbs, and Tom at 205 lbs.. How much total weight would they have to lose from the last weigh in to make their new weights exactly?

A. 17 1/8 lbs   B. 347 lbs   C. 18 3/8 lbs.   D. 19 1/8 lbs

LESSON #18   FRACTIONS

WARMUPS

1. 44.4 − 5
2. 44.4 − 50
3. 44.4 − .5

4. 8 − 5 5/8
5. 3⅓ × 4/5
6. 25% of $60

7. $60.00
   × .25
8. 3¾ ÷ 5

9. (⅔)³
10. √625

SOLVE THE FOLLOWING:

11. $T + 13⅓ = 20$ 12. $¾T + 7 = 22$ 13. $9/T = 3/⅔$

The school year consists of 180 days for the following five problems.

PROBLEM #14
Eighty-eight days out of 180 school days are over. What fraction of the school year is left?
   A. 22/45   B. 88/180   C. 82/180   D. 23/45

PROBLEM #15
If 7/30 of the school year is over, how many school days are left?
   A. 42 days   B. 138 days   C. 23 days   D. Not enough information

PROBLEM #16
If 1/4 of the school year is over and another 1/3 goes by, how many total days of school are over?
   A. A. 25 5/7 days   B. 105 days   C. 120 days   d. 75 days

PROBLEM #17
If 4/5 of the school year is over, what fraction would be over after six more school days?
   A. 7/8   B. 30 days   C. 150 days   D. 5/6

PROBLEM #18
If 5/9 of the school year is over and ten more days go by, how many school days are left?
   A. 40 days   B. 7/18   C. 70 days   D. 110 days

(**18**)

LESSON #19   FRACTIONS

WARMUPS
1. 51.12 − 60
2. 51.12 − 6
3. 51.12 − .6
4. 1/2 of $36?
5. 3/4 of $36?
6. 2/3 of $36?
7. 13 1/2 ÷ 9/10
8. 25 − 13 1/3
9. $(3/4)^4$
10. $\sqrt{9/25}$

SOLVE THE FOLLOWING:
11. 24 / U = ⅔ / 6   **12.** ½ C + 15 = 22   **13.** 40L + 30 = 60

PROBLEM #14
Samuel is a carpenter. He builds a variety of things. He was hired to build a triangular fence. The sides were: 16 1/2 ft., 13 3/4 ft., and 14 2/3 ft.. How much fence material did Samuel need?
A. 43 2/3 ft. B. 43 11/12 ft. C. 44 11/12 ft. D. 44 2/3 ft.

PROBLEM #15
On another project Samuel has a 15 1/2 ft. two by four. He needs to cut a 6 7/12 ft. piece and a 3 1/4 ft piece. How much will he have left over?
A. 9 5/6 ft. B. 5 2/3 ft. C. 25 1/3 ft. D. 8 11/12 ft.

PROBLEM #16
Samuel's specialty is fences. He has a standard sized fence he likes to build. It's perimeter is 76⅔ ft. If Samuel builds eight of these fences, how many feet of material does he need?
A. A. 613 1/3 ft. B. 68 2/3 ft. C. 608 2/3 ft.   D. 84 2/3 ft.

PROBLEM #17
Another fence that Samuel built was rectangular. Two of the sides are 20 1/4 ft. each. If the other two sides are 10 3/8 ft. each, what is the perimeter of the fence?
A. 30 5/8 ft. B. 210 3/64 ft. C. 9 7/8 ft. D. 61 1/4 ft.

PROBLEM #18
What is the area enclosed in the fence in Problem #17?
A. 105 3/64 sq. ft   B. 210 3/32 sq. ft.
C. 420 3/64 sq. ft.   D. 52 35/64 sq. ft.

Just think how much **teacher preparation time** a **classroom set** of Practice Practice Practice will save you?????????

LESSON 20 FRACTIONS

WARMUPS
1. $37.1 - 6$ 4. $8 - 5\ 1/4$ 7. $4\ 1/5 \times 1\ 3/7$ 9. $(1/2)^4$
2. $37.1 - 60$ 5. $4\ 3/4 + 3\ 2/3$ 8. $24 \div .0006$ 10. $\sqrt{9/100}$
3. $37.1 - .6$ 6. $7\ 1/2 \div 15$

SOLVE THE FOLLOWING:
11. $9U - 7\ 1/3 = 19\ 2/3$
12. $.05C + 8 = 6$
13. $15 / 24 = L / 16$

PROBLEM #14
Find the product of 2 1/3 and 3/10.
   A. 2 1/10   B. 7/10
   C. 2 19/30   D. 7 7/9

PROBLEM #15
What is the difference of 8 1/5 and 6 1/6?
   A. 14 2/11   B. 14 11/30
   C. 50 17/30 D. 2 1/30

PROBLEM #16
What is the quotient of 6 2/5 and 1 3/5?
   A. 6 6/25   B. 4
   C. 8   D. 10 6/25

PROBLEM #17
Find the sum of 3 4/9 and 6 7/12.
   A. 9 11/21   B. 3 5/36
   C. 10 1/36   D. 124/237

PROBLEM #18
What is the product of 7/10 and the sum of 1 1/2 and 3/4?
   A. 2 19/20   B. 14/45
   C. 12 3/40   D. 1 13/20

(20)

LESSON #21   FRACTIONS

WARMUPS
1. 24.42 – 4
2. 24.42 – .4
3. 24.42 – 40
4. 4 1/2 ÷ 9/10
5. 75% of $60
6. 3/4 of $60
7. 8 – 5 7/9
8. .004 ÷ 5
9. $(10)^5$
10. $\sqrt{625}$

SOLVE THE FOLLOWING:
11. 12 / **B** = 15 / 35   12. 8 / **R** = ¾ / 9   13. 6U – 36 = 72

Martha decided to make some things to eat and drink for a party. She had recipes for the things she was making.

PROBLEM #14
The punch recipe called for 4 cups of sugar. Martha thought this was too sweet and only put in ⅓ as much sugar. How much sugar did Martha put in the punch?
   A. 12 cups   B. ⅔ cup   C. 1⅓ cups D. 1⅔ cups

PROBLEM #15
The recipe she had for cupcakes made 12 cupcakes. Martha wanted to make 36. The recipe called for 2½ cups of flour. How much flour did Martha need for 36 cupcakes?
  A. 7 1/2 cups   B. 5 cups   C. 5/6 cup   D. 10 cups

PROBLEM #16
Another recipe Martha was using called for 1⅓ cups of milk and 2¼ cups of water. How much liquid was this?
   A. 3 cups   B. 11/12 cups   C. 3 7/12 cups   D. 3 1/12 cups

PROBLEM #17
Martha expected 21 people at her party. She decided that each person would drink about 2⅓ cups of punch. How much punch did she think she needed?
   A. 49 cups   B. 23 1/3 cups   C. 18 2/3 cups   D. 42 2/3 cups

PROBLEM #18
The main dish Martha was making had a recipe that called for 2½ cups of tomato sauce for six servings. She needed 21 servings. How much tomato sauce did she need?
   A. 7 1/2 cups   B. 8 3/4 cups   C. 29 1/2 cups   D. 52 1/2 cups

(21)

LESSON #22   FRACTIONS

WARMUPS
1. $47.09 - 7$ 4. $21 - 8 3/4$ 7. $6 1/2 + 7 3/4$ 9. $(2/3)^3$
2. $47.09 - 70$ 5. $6 2/3 \times 9/10$ 8. 25% of $48   10. $\sqrt{25/36}$
3. $47.09 - .7$ 6. $24/25 \div 1 1/3$

SOLVE THE FOLLOWING PROBLEMS:
11. $7K - 24 = 39$ 12. $9N = 2N - 28$ 13. $20 / 35 = 16 / M$

PROBLEM #14
Bruce was digging post holes. His fence posts were 8 ft. long. He wanted to bury 2¼ ft. of each post. How much of the fence post would be sticking up out of the ground?
  A. 10¼ ft B. 6¾ ft.   C. 5¾ ft.   D. 6¼ ft.

PROBLEM #15
Bruce planned on digging 9 holes all at the same 2¼ ft. depth. How many feet would Bruce have to dig?
  A. 18 1/4 ft. B. 20 1/4 ft.   C. 20 ft.   D. 19 3/4 ft.

PROBLEM #16
Because of rocks and hard soil, Bruce found he could not make all the holes the same. The first four holes were 2 1/4 ft., 2 1/3 ft., 2 ft., and 1 7/8 ft.. At this point, how many feet had Bruce dug?
  A. 7 23/24 ft.   B. 7 11/24 ft. C. 7 3/5 ft. D. 8 11/24 ft.

PROBLEM #17
After Bruce put all nine posts in the ground he figured he dug a total of 19 1/8 ft.. What was the average depth of each hole?
  A. 2 1/8 ft.   B. 28 1/8 ft. C. 1 7/8 ft. D. 2 1/4 ft.

PROBLEM #18
Using problem #17, what was the total length of all 9 posts sticking up out of the ground?
  A. 52 1/8 ft. B. 28 1/8 ft.   C. 52 7/8 ft. D. 53 7/8 ft.

(22)

LESSON #23   INTEGERS

WARMUPS
1. 34.2 – 4
4. -8 + -4 – (-12)
7. .24 ÷ 600
9. $(-3)^4$
2. 34.2 – 40
5. -8 × -5 ÷ 10
8. 7½ – 8
10. $\sqrt{144}$
3. 34.2 – .4
6. 7 – 8½

SOLVE THE FOLLOWING:
11. **K** + 24 = 17
12. **A** + 24 = 17 3/5
13. 24/32 = **T**/-44

PROBLEM #14
The temperature in Soap Lake was 85 degrees F on a Thursday in July. On Friday it went up a positive 13 degrees F. What was the temperature on Friday?
  A. 72 degrees   B. 108 degrees   C. 98 degrees   D. 62 degrees

PROBLEM #15
On a Thursday, six months later it was negative 8 degrees F. What was the difference in the two Thursdays' temperatures?
  A. 106 degrees   B. 93 degrees   C. 77 degrees   D. -77 degrees

PROBLEM #16
The temperature in Soap Lake was -8 degrees on a Thursday in February. On Friday it dropped 12 degrees. What was the temperature on Friday?
  A. 20 degrees   B. -4 degrees   C. 4 degrees   D. -20 degrees

PROBLEM #17
The next week on Tuesday it was -2 degrees. The next Thursday the temperature was four times colder than Tuesday. What was the temperature on Thursday?
  A. 6 degrees   B. -8 degrees   C. 8 degrees   D. -6 degrees

PROBLEM #18
In a five day span, Soap Lake's temperatures were: 6 degrees, -2 degrees, -8 degrees, 0 degrees, and 14 degrees. What was the average temperature for this five day span?
  A. 10 degrees   B. 6 degrees   C. 2 degrees   D. -6 degrees

(23)

LESSON #24   INTEGERS

WARMUPS
1. $21.1 - 7$ 4. $-8 + -4$ 7. $-8\frac{1}{2} \times -6$ 9. $(-2)^5$
2. $21.1 - 70$ 5. $-8 - (-4)$ 8. $-24 \div .008$ 10. $\sqrt{400}$
3. $.7 - 21.1$ 6. $-31 - (-21\frac{2}{3})$

SOLVE THE FOLLOWING:
11. $4F + 36 = -8$ 12. $9I = 18 + 12I$ 13. $15/20 = 45/T$

PROBLEM #14
Stan was a running back for the Buckhorn Rhino's football team.
In one game he carried the ball five times for an average of 7 yards a
carry. What were his total yards?
    A. 1.4 yds.   B. 12 yds.   C. 35 yds.   D. 14 yds.

PROBLEM #15
In another game, Stan carried the ball seven times. He gained:
11yds., -3 yds., 5 yds., -6 yds., 15 yds., 0 yds., and 75 yds.. How
many yards short of a hundred yard rushing game was he?
    A. 97 yds.   B. 14 yds.   C. 3 yds.   D. Stan was over 100 yds.

PROBLEM #16
The quarterback for the Rhinos was Scott. Scott was sacked 4
times for losses in one game. He was sacked for -4 yds., -8 yds.,
-2 yds., and -10 yds.. What was his average loss per sack?
    A. -6 yds.   B. -24 yds.   C. 16 yds. D. -12 yds.

PROBLEM #17
Stan and Scott accounted for all the yards for the Rhinos in
one game. Stan rushed for 102 yards. Scott passed for 240 yards
and ran for 38 yards not including the five times he was sacked.
If the team had 352 total yards, how many yards did Scott lose
on sacks?
    A. 38 yards   B. -38 yards   C. -28 yards   D. None

PROBLEM #18
Stan, in one half, ran the ball 6 times. In his first 5 rushes he
had runs of 10 yds., -6 yds., 14 yds., 7 yds., and 22 yds.. If he
averaged 7 yds. a carry for the first half, how much did he gain
on his 6th run?
    A. 7 yds.   B. 1 yd.   C. -15 yds.   D. -5 yds.

(24)

LESSON #25   RATIONALS

WARMUPS
1. 26.8 – 6
2. 26.8 – 60
3 26½ – 60

4. 4½ × -⅔
5. -18 ÷ -¾
6. -8 + -7 – 15

7. .0024 ÷ 12
8. 12 ÷ .0024

9. $(-⅓)^3$
10. $\sqrt{81}$

SOLVE THE FOLLOWING:
11. 20T – 5T = .45   12. 14/I = 35/25   13. ⅔M + 18 = 8

PROBLEM #14
Tommy's Golf Service's stock started at 6 1/8 on Monday morning. It dropped 2 1/2 points that day. What did it end up at the end of the day?

A. 8 5/8   B. -4 3/8   C. 4 3/8   D. 3 5/8

PROBLEM #15
On Tuesday through Friday Tommy's Golf Service's stock went: + 3 1/4, - 1 1/4, -2 1/8, and +3/8. What was it's net gain for the week (including Monday)?

A. - 2 1/4   B. + 7 1/2   C. - 10   D. + 1/4

PROBLEM #16
John bought 500 shares of Tommy's stock at $5.50 a share. If the stock gained 2 1/4 on August 10th, how much did John earn on that day?

A. -$1,625   B. +$3,875   C. +$12.38   D. +$1,125

PROBLEM #17
John's stock which started at $5.50 a share went -2, - 1/4, and + 3/4 on three consecutive days. How much was each share of John's original purchase worth?

A. $4.00   B. $2,000   C. -$1.50   D. $7.00

PROBLEM #18
John also bought stock in Steve's Dive Shop. He paid $2,890.00 in buying $8.50 per share stock. If the stock went down - 1/4 per share, how much was John's purchase worth?

A. $2,805   B. $2,976   C. $8,750   D. $2,775.50

(25)

LESSON #26   TIME

WARMUPS
1. 29.3 − 5
2. 29.3 − 50
3. 29.3 − .5
4. $60 × .8
5. 80% of $60?
6. $60 ÷ .8
7. ⅔ × 60
8. $ 60.50
   × ___ .4
9. 4^3
10. √81

SOLVE THE FOLLOWING
11. 4T + 31 = 71   12. 9E − 40 = 4E   13. 4 / X = 6 / 9

PROBLEM #14
How long did these three Longview students spend on their homework last night all together?   Darci spent 1 hour, 20 minutes, Lisa spent 48 minutes and Rody spent 1 hour, 10 minutes.
A. 4 hours, 8 min.   B. 2 hours, 58 min.
C. 3 hours, 18 min.   D. 3 hours, 38 min.

PROBLEM #15
Taylor from Raymondsville spent 35 minutes on his homework last night. How much more time did Darci spend on her homework than Taylor?
A. 1 hour, 25 min.   B. 45 min.
C. 1 hour, 55 min.   D. 55 min.

PROBLEM #16
If Darci started at 6:45 and took no breaks, what time did she finish?
A. 8:05   B. 7:55   C. 7:05   D. 8:15

PROBLEM #17
Lisa started her homework, but took a half hour break to watch cartoons before finishing her homework. If she started at 7:15, what time did she finish her homework?
A. 7:13   B. 8:03   C. 8:33   D. 9:03

PROBLEM #18
Rody was doing math and she spent all her time working 14 problems. On average, how long did she work on each problem?
A. 4 min.   B. 5 min.   C. 7 min.   D. 8 min

(26)

LESSON #27   TIME
WARMUPS
1. 14.7 − 6
2. 14.7 − 60
3. 14.7 − .6
4. $40 x 1.2
5. $40 ÷ .005
6. .02 ÷ 50
7. ¾ x $40
8. 15 ÷ ¾
9. 5^3
10. $\sqrt{144}$

SOLVE THE FOLLOWING
11. T + 43 = 30   **12.** 10 / 15 = T / 45   **13.** What is the perimeter and area of a rectangle six feet by eight feet?

PROBLEM #14
Julio and Sara work for the Acme Construction Company of Weslaco. On one project in Edinburg they each worked 10 hours, 42 minutes. How much time did they work together?
   A. 20 hours 84 minutes   B.   21 hours, 34 minutes
   C. 21 hours, 24 minutes   D. 20 hours, 24 minutes.

PROBLEM #15
On another project Julio and Sara were joined by Ben from Harlingen. When the project was complete, Julio had worked 7 hours, 45 minutes, Sara 10 hours, 45 minutes, and Ben 12½ hours. How long did it take these three to complete the project?
 A. 30 hours   B. 29½ hours   C. 30 hours, 45 minutes   D. 31 hours

PROBLEM #16
Jasmine and Sam from Pharr were added to the other three workers on the next job. If they all were expected to work the same amount, how long would each work on an 84 hour job?
   A. 16 hours, 48 minutes   B. 42 hours
   C. 16 hours, 50 minutes   D. 420 hours

PROBLEM #17
A job in La Joya called for only four workers. They each worked exactly the same number of hours. If they each worked 28 hours, 40 minutes; how long did the job take?
   A. 112 hours, 40 min.   B. 112 hours, 16 min.
   C. 114 hours, 40 min.   D.   7 hours, 10 min.

PROBLEM #18
Sam worked 6 hours, 20 minutes on a project in San Benito. Jasmine worked 7 hours, 15 minutes and Ben worked 8 hours, 46 minutes on the same project. What was the average number of hours worked by these three?
   A. 11 hours, 11 min. B. 22 hours, 21 min.
   C. 7 hours, 27 min.   D.   5 hours, 35 min.

LESSON # 28 TIME (CONVERSION)

WARMUPS

1. 56.13 − 7   4. 180 ÷ 60   6. 8¼ − 5 ⅓   9. 10^6
2. 56.13 − 70   5. $55.12   7. 80% of $45   10. √900
3. 56.13 − 7.7   × ___.75   8. 4 1/2 × 8/9

SOLVE THE FOLLOWING

11. 25 / M = 20 / 100   **12.** 14 = 40% OF ?   **13.** 8M − 20 = 64

A student name Tony Seconda liked time measurement. He liked to measure things in seconds.

PROBLEM #14

A friend said to meet him in 20 minutes. How many seconds did Tony have to wait to meet his friend?
   A. ⅓ second   B. 300 sec.   C. 1,200 sec.   D. 2,000 sec.

PROBLEM #15

Tony boiled an egg for 330 seconds. How many minutes was this?
   A. 55 minutes   B. 19,800 minutes   C. 11 minutes   D. 5½ minutes

PROBLLEM #16

A paper Tony wrote for Mr. Smith's class took him 2 hours and 10 minutes. When Tony counted up the seconds, what did he come up with?
   A. 7,800 sec.   B. 720 sec.   C. 9,600 sec.   D. 1,800 sec.

PROBLEM #17

Tony heard that a professional basketball player got paid a lot of money. He estimated that the player got $8,100 a game. The professional basketball player played 45 minutes in last night's game. How much did he earn per second in last nights game?
   A. $3,00   B. $27.00   C. $2.70   D. $81.00

PROBLEM #18

Tony's mother's maiden name was Weekly. She asked Tony how many seconds were in a week to keep him busy for a while. What answer should Tony have given her?
   A. 25,200 sec.   B. 86,400 sec.   C. 604,800 sec.   D. 432,000 sec.

LESSON #29   TIME
WARMUPS
1. $34.56 - 8$ 2. $34.56 - .8$ 3. $34.56 - 80$ 4. $24 \div .06$ 5. $.06 \div 24$
6. $7 \ 1/2 \times 4/5$ 7. $3 \ 1/3 \div 5$ 8. $9 - 6 \ 3/4$ 9. 2^4 10. $\sqrt{81}$

SOLVE THE FOLLOWING
11. $T + 44 = 40$ 12. $3I - 8 = 28$ 13. $10M - 30 = 3M + 5$

There are four time zones across the United States. From west to east they're called Pacific, Mountain, Central and Eastern. There is a one hour time change between each zone. The Pacific Time Zone is 3 hours behind the Eastern Time Zone. Some cities in each time zone are:
PACIFIC (Seattle, Spokane, Portland, LA, San Francisco, San Diego, Sacramento)
MOUNTAIN (Denver, Albuquerque, Phoenix, Boise, Billings, Missoula, Tucson)
CENTRAL (Dallas, Chicago, Minneapolis, New Orleans, St. Louis, KC, Houston)
EASTERN (New York, Boston, Philadelphia, Pittsburgh, Washington, Atlanta, Miami,
   Orlando, Cleveland, Baltimore, Detroit, Charlotte, Birmingham, Tampa, Richmond)

PROBLEM #14
   If it is 2:30 AM in New York, what time is it in Los Angeles?
   A. 11:30 AM   B. 5:30 AM   C. 5:30 PM   D. 11:30 PM

PROBLEM #15
   If it is 4:15 PM in the Mountain Time Zone, what time is it in the
Central Time Zone?
   A. 5:15 PM   B. 3:15 PM   C. 6:15 PM   D. 2:15 PM

PROBLEM #16
   Ms. Sharp drove two hours from the Pacific Time Zone into the
Mountain Time Zone. If she left at 8:23 AM, what time was it when
she arrived?
   A. 10:23 AM   B. 9:23 AM   C. 11:23 AM   D. 12:23 PM

PROBLEM #17
   A flight left the Eastern Time Zone at 7:30 PM and landed in the
Mountain Time Zone. If it was a 5 hour, 15 minute flight; what time
did the plane land?
   A. 12:45 AM   B. 11:15 PM   C. 10:45 PM   D. 9:45 PM

PROBLEM #18
   Ms. Krueger flew from the Pacific Time Zone to the Eastern Time
Zone. She was in the air for six hours, thirty-five minutes. She then drove
to the Central Time Zone which took 3 hours, twenty minutes. She left at
10:30 AM. What time was it when she finished her travels?
   A. 11:25 PM   B. 10:25 PM   C. 12:05 AM   D. 8:15 PM

(29)

LESSON #30   TIME

WARMUPS
1. 71.18 – 6   4. .2 ÷ 80   7. 15 – 9 2/9   9. 2^6
2. 71.18 – .6   5. 80 ÷ .2   8. $60.50   10. $\sqrt{16}$
3. 71.18 – 60   6. 5/6 × 9/10   <u>×   .05</u>

SOLVE THE FOLLOWING:
11. U / 14 = 12 / 21   **12.** 5C – 21 = 59   **13.** 8L = 2L + 42

TIME ZONE INFORMATION IS IN LESSON #29
PROBLEM #14
   Ken from Minnetonka left Minneapolis at 11:30 AM and flew to New York. What time was it in New York when he arrived if the flight took 2 hours and 45 minutes?
   A. 12:30 PM   B. 8:30 PM   C. 3:15 PM   D. 3:45 PM

PROBLME #15
   Tice of Stewart, Florida left Orlando at 7:45 AM. He flew to Seattle. If the flight took four hours and 25 minutes, what time did Tice land in Seattle?
   A. 9:10 AM   B. 3:10 PM   C. 12:10 PM D. 10:10 AM

PROBLEM #16
   Drew drove 2 hours and 40 minutes from his home in West Virginia to the Pittsburgh Airport. He then flew to Phoenix to watch Stanford win the NCAA Basketball Regional. The flight took 4 hours and 10 minutes. If he left his home in West Virginia at 7:15 AM, what time did he get to Phoenix?
   A. 2:05 PM   B. 11:55 AM   C. 12:55 PM   D. 12:05 PM

PROBLEM #17
   Greg left his home in Bothel at 8:15 PM and drove 41 minutes to SeaTac Airport in Seattle. He waited one hour, twenty-three minutes in the terminal and then flew to Atlanta. It took Greg one hour, twelve minutes to get to his work in Roswell from the airport. If the flight from Seattle to Atlanta took 5 hours, 13 minutes, what time did Greg get to work?
   A. 7:44 AM   B. 12:12 PM   C. 6:21 AM   D. 6:32 AM

PROBLEM #18
   Jackie from Savage made the mistake of letting her older sister Ginger from St. Cloud make their travel reservations from Minneapolis to Portland, Oregon. Ginger found a real bargain and bought tickets for herself and Jackie. This was their flight schedule: Minneapolis to Houston - 2 hr., 55 min.; layover in Houston - 1hr., 10 min.; Houston to Denver - 1 hr., 41 min.; layover in Denver - 2 hr., 28 min.; Denver to Portland 2 hr., 18 min.; drive to their middle sister Kathy's house in Longview, Washington - 55 min.. If Ginger and Jackie left Minneapolis on Ginger's birthday (April 1st) at 7:40 PM, what time did they get to their sister Kathy's house?
   A. 9:07 AM   B. 6:12 AM   C. 7:07 AM   D. 5:07 AM

(**30**)

LESSON #31   TOURNAMENT MATH

WARMUPS

1. $71.7 - 8$ 4. $.08 \div 400$ 7. 25% of $48   9. 4^3

2. $71.7 - .8$ 5. $2\ 2/3 \times 8/9$ 8. $71.11   10. $\sqrt{121}$

3. $71.7 - 80$ 6. $9 - 4\frac{1}{3}$ $\times \quad .08$

SOLVE THE FOLLOWING:

11. $8W - 13 = 35$ **12.** $35 / 25 = 28 / S$ **13.** $15 = 75\%$ of ?

TOURNAMENT MATH -

1. To run a tournament you need a number of teams equal to a power of 2. Ex. $2^1 = $**2**, $2^2 = $**4**, $2^3 = $**8**, etc.

2. If you do **NOT** have a number of teams equal to a power of two, you add **BYES** to reach the next **HIGHER POWER OF TWO.** Ex. If you have seven teams, you add **ONE BYE** to make 8 teams.

PROBLEM #14

You can run a tournament with four or eight teams. What are the next two numbers greater than eight that you can use for a tournament?
A. 10, 12   B. 12, 16   C. 16, 24   D. 16, 32

PROBLEM #15

After your answer on PROBLEM #14, what are the next two number of teams you can use for a tournament?
A. 64, 128   B. 48, 64   C. 64, 120   D. 32, 48

PROBLEM #16

If you have 25 teams for a tournament, how many **BYES** do you need to add to run the tournament?
A. 3   B. 7   C. 9   D. 15

PROBLEM #17

The **NFL** (National Football League) puts twelve teams into their **SUPER BOWL TOURNAMENT.** How many byes do they use?
A. 2   B. 6   C. 4   D. 8

PROBLEM #18

The Texas State Barbecue Tournament in Austin has room for 50 teams. How many **BYES** are there in the Texas State Barbecue Tournament?
A. 14   B. 18   C. 6   D. 2

LESSON # 32   TOURNAMENT MATH

WARMUPS

1. $52.7 - 60$ 4. $.084 \div 12$ 7. 75% of $64   9. 10^4
2. $52.7 - 6$ 5. $5\ 1/3 \times 9/16$ 8. $51.71   10. $\sqrt{144}$
3. $52.7 - .6$ 6. $8 - 5\frac{3}{4}$ $\times\ .008$

SOLVE THE FOLLOWING

11. $5T - 24 = 71$ **12.** $8\ /\ I = 20\ /\ 15$ **13.** $35 =$?% of 56?

TOURNAMENT MATH - Look at Lesson # 31.

PROBLEM #14

There are only certain numbers of teams that will make a tournament come out even. The first three numbers are: 2, 4, and 8. What are the next three numbers greater than 8 which will make a tournament come out even?

A. 12, 16, 20   B. 10, 14, 18   C. 24, 32, 40   D. 16, 32, 64

PROBLEM #15

What are the next two tournament numbers after the three in the answer to Problem #14?

A. 128, 256   B. 48, 64   C. 64, 128   D. 80, 120

PROBLEM #16

The Koch Family from St. Cloud has 13 entries into the Koch Family Cribbage Championships next June. How many byes will they need to make their tournament come out even?

A. 5   B. 3   C. 21   D. 7

PROBLEM #17

Back in the early 1980's the NCAA Men's College Basketball Tournament invited 48 teams. How many byes did they need?

A. 2   B. 8   C. 16   D. 12

PROBLEM #18

Pat from Baytown was running the "Brown & Root" Company Golf Tournament. It was One on One Match Play Tournament on consecutive Saturday mornings starting March 6th. How many byes will Pat need to run the tournament if he has 27 entries? How many consecutive Saturdays will he need?

A. 5 byes, 4 Saturdays   B. 4 byes, 4 Saturdays
C. 5 byes, 5 Saturdays   D. 4 byes, 5 Saturdays

LESSON #33   TOURNAMENT MATH
WARMUPS
1. $42.71 – $5   4. 1/2 of $24   7. 4 1/2 ÷ 9/10   9. 5^3
2. $42.71 – $.55   5. 2/3 of $24   8. 25% of $24   10. $\sqrt{36}$
3. $42.21 – $50   6. $84 ÷ .04

SOLVE THE FOLLOWING:
11. 2T + 14 = 20   **12.** 12 / 18 = T / 27   **13.** 25% of ? = 12.

Read **TOURNAMENT MATH ON LESSON #31.** The 2004 Mens College NCAA Basketball Tournament started with 64 teams. When a team loses it is out of the tournament. One half of the teams played on Thursday, March 18th. Those that won played on Saturday, March 20th. The other half of the 64 teams played on Friday, March 19th with the winners playing again on Sunday, March 21st.

Half the remaining teams played again on Thursday, March 25th, with the winners playing on Saturday, March 27th. The other half of the remaining teams played on Friday, March 26th, with the winners playing again on Sunday, March 28th.

The four remaining teams played on Saturday, April 3rd, and Monday, April 5th, to determine the Champion.

PROBLEM #14
How many **BYES** were used in the 2004 Mens NCAA College Basketball Tournament?
    A. 2   B. 4   C. 36   D. 0

PROBLEM #15
After half the teams in the 2004 Mens NCAA College Basketball Tournament had played their games on Thursday, March 18th, how many of the 64 teams remained in the tournament?
    A. 32   B. 40   C. 42   D. 48

PROBLEM #16
After all the 1ST round games were played Friday night, March 19th, how many teams were still in the tournament?
    A. 32   B. 48   C. 16   D. 24

PROBLEM #17
After all the games were played a week later on Friday, March 26th, how many teams were still left in the tournament?
    A. 6   B. 16   C. 12   D. 8

PROBLEM #18
Sixty-four teams started the NCAA Tournament. How many of the 64 teams lost the last game they played in the tournament?
    A. 32   B. 48   C. 63   D. 16

LESSON #34   TOURNAMENT MATH

WARMUPS
1. $23.44 – $5   4. .04 ÷ 80   7. 80 ÷ .04   9. 2^6
2. $23.44 – $50   5. 9 1/3 × 3/7   8. 9⅓ – 4¾   10. $\sqrt{64}$
3. $23.44 – $.55   6. 24 – 13⅔

SOLVE THE FOLLOWING:
11. 8N = 2N – 42   **12.** 9C + 35 = 4C   **13.** What is the perimeter and area of a right triangle with legs of 15 ft. and 20 ft., and a hypotenuse of 25 ft.?

TOURNAMENT MATH - Read the Tournament Math information on lessons #31 and #33.

PROBLEM #14
The Texas AAA Soccer Tournament had 26 teams. How many byes did this tournament have to use to make the tournament come out even?
   A. 4   B. 10   C. 2   D. 6

PROBLEM #15
After all the 2004 Mens NCAA College Basketball Tournament games were finished on Sunday, March 21st, how many teams were still left in the tournament?
   A. 32   B. 24   C. 16   D. 8

PROBLEM #16
After all the Saturday, March 27th, games were over, how many teams were still in the tournament?
   A. 12   B. 6   C. 8   D. 4

PROBLEM #17
After all the NCAA Basketball games were played on Saturday, April 3rd, how many teams were still in the tournament?
   A. 1   B. 2   C. 3   D. 4

PROBLEM #18
UCONN won the 2004 Mens NCAA Basketball Tournament. How many games did they win in the tournament?
   A. 4   B. 5   C. 6   D 8

(**34**)

WARMUPS
1. $56.19 - 7$ 4. $75.40   6. $24 \div .0003$ 9. 2^5
2. $56.19 - .9$ $\times \quad .08$ 7. $12 - 7\frac{3}{4}$ 10. $\sqrt{100}$
3. $56.19 - 70$ 5. $3\frac{1}{3} \times 18$ 8. 80% of $75.40?

SOLVE THE FOLLOWING:
11. $14 / A = 21 / 9$ 12. $13 / 25 = N / 100$ 13. $3N + 39 = 24$

TOURNAMENT MATH
   1. Read the TOURNAMENT MATH SECTIONS on Lessons **#31 & #33.**
   2. **SEEDING -** The 64 teams in the 2004 NCAA Mens College Basketball
Tournament are split into 4 **REGIONS OF 16 TEAMS EACH.** In each
REGION the **#1 SEED PLAYS THE #16 SEED, THE #2 SEED PLAYS
THE #15 SEED, ETC.**

PROBLEM #14
   In each of the 4 regions what seed does the # 5 seed play?
   A. #10   B. #11   C. #12   D. #13

PROBLEM #15
   The #9 seed in each region will play the   ?   seed.
   A. #6   B. #12   C. #10   D. #8

PROBLEM #16
   The Friday Night 3 on 3 Basketball Tournament at the Alondra Park Gym in
Lawndale had 11 teams sign up last Friday night. How many byes did they need?
   A. 3   B. 5   C. 7   D. 21

PROBLEM #17
   Illinois won their 2nd game in the 2004 NCAA Mens College Basketball
Tournament on Sunday, March 21st. This was the end of the 2nd round of games.
How many of the other 63 teams that started the tournament with Illinois were
still in the tournament?
   A. 15   B. 47   C. 31   D. 32

PROBLEM #18
   The team (Georgia Tech) that took 2nd place in the 2004 Mens College NCAA
Basketball Tournament lost their last game in the tournament to the 1st place team
(UCONN). How many games did Georgia Tech win in the tournament?
   A. 3   B. 6   C. 4   D. 5

LESSON #36   PROPORTION (STORY FIRST)

WARMUPS
1. 29.1 − 7
2. 29.1 − .7
3. 29.1 − 70
4. 40% of $95.15
5. 2/5 × $95.15
6. .04 ÷ 8
7. 7 − 4 1/8
8. 7 1/2 × 4/5
9. 10^3
10. $\sqrt{400}$

SOLVE THE FOLLOWING PROPORTIONS
11. 12 / 15 = N / 25 **12.** 6 / 14 = 15 / T   **13.** .003 / R = 6 / .04

Ric and Terri left San Antonio in their new blue Volkswagon sedan at 6:00am. They arrived in New Orleans at 3:00pm. They stopped in Houston one hour for breakfast. Ric drove three fourths of the way. It is 200 miles from San Antonio to Houston and 360 miles from Houston to New Orleans. Use this information to solve problems one thru five below.

PROBLEM #14
How many miles did Ric drive? How many miles did Terri drive?
A. 420 miles Ric drove;   140 miles Terri drove.
B. 350 miles Ric drove;   210 miles Terri drove.
C. 400 miles Ric drove;   160 miles Terri drove.
D. 360 miles Ric drove;   200 miles Terri drove.

PROBLEM #15
How long did Terri drive? How long did Ric drive?
A. Terri drove 6 hours;   Ric drove 2 hours.
B. Terri drove 2 hours;   Ric drove 6 hours.
C. Terri drove 2 hours; 15 min: Ric drove 6 hours 45 min.
D. Terri drove 6 hour; 45 min: Ric drove 2 hours 15 min.

PROBLEM #16
About how fast were Ric & Terri driving when they were not eating breakfast?
A. 55 mph. B. 62 mph.   C. 70 mph.   D. 75 mph.

PROBLEM #17
About what time did Ric & Terri eat breakfast in Houston?
A. 8:30am   B. 9:15am   C. 10:00am   D. 10:30am

PROBLEM #18
Ric and Terri's volkswagon gets 30 miles to a gallon of gas. How many gallons of gas did they need to drive from San Antonio to New Orleans?
A. 15 gallons   B. 19 gallons   C. 23 gallons   D. 12 gallons

LESSON #37   PROPORTION (STORY FIRST)

WARMUPS
1. 29.7 – 6
2. 29.7 – 60
3. 1/2 of $76

4. 3.6 ÷ .009
5. $95.45
$\underline{\times \quad .06}$

6. 5 2/5 ÷ 9/10
7. -7 – (-9) + -2
8. -8 × 5 ÷ -4

9. 5^4
10. $\sqrt{1/25}$

SOLVE THE FOLLOWING:
11. 3 / 7 = 21 / N   **12.** 20 / 30 = N / 9   **13.** 48 / 42 = 32 / N

USE THE FOLLOWING INFORMATION FOR PROBLEMS 14-18.

The Campbells drove the 863 miles from Austin to St. Louis in two days. Both Doug and Kris drove their Acura at 66 mph.. They left Austin on Wednesday morning at 8:30 am and drove the 200 miles to Dallas where they stopped for an hour for lunch. They then drove the 262 miles from Dallas to Tulsa where they stopped for the night. The Campbells left Tulsa Thursday morning at 8:00 am and drove the 192 miles to Springfield, Mo. where they had lunch. They took an hour for lunch and then drove the rest of the way home to St. Louis.

PROBLEM #14
About what time did the Campbells eat lunch in Dallas?
A. 10:30 am   B. 11:00 am   C. 11:30 am   D. 12:00 noon

PROBLEM #15
About what time did the Campbells get to Tulsa?
A. 3:00 pm   B. 3:30 pm   C. 4:00 pm   D. 4:30 pm

PROBLEM #16
About how many miles is it from Springfield to St. Louis?
A. 104 miles   B. 109miles   C. 192 miles   D. 154 miles

PROBLEM #17
About what time did the Campbells get home in St. Louis?
A. 2:15 pm   B. 3:15 pm   C. 3:45 pm   D. 4:15 pm

PROBLEM #18
Doug drove 4/5ths of the way from Austin to St. Louis. Kris drove the rest of the way. Approximately how many miles did Doug drive? Approximately how many miles did Kris drive?
A. Doug 750 miles, Kris 110 mi.   B. Doug 420 miles, Kris 440 mi.
C. Doug 645 miles, Kris 215 mi.   D. Doug 690 miles, Kris 170 mi.

(37)

LESSON #38   PROPORTIONS   (STORY FIRST)

WARMUPS
1. $50.06 - 6$
2. $50.06 - .6$
3. $50.06 - 60$

4. $\$60.80$
5. $3\ 1/2 \times 6$

$\times\ .25$

6. 25% of $\$60.80$
7. $5 - 3\ 5/6$
8. $1/4 \times \$60.80$

9. 3^4
10. $\sqrt{196}$

SOLVE THE FOLLOWING:
11. $15 = 60\%$ of ?   12. $8T + 10 = 50$ 13. $12 / 9 = T / 6$

Shannon and Scott drove back to college after Thanksgiving at their folks' house in Castle Rock. They left home at 6:30 am and drove the 325 miles to Pullman, Washington. They stopped one hour and 15 minutes for lunch in Pasco. They then drove on to Pullman where Scott attends Washington State University. Shannon spent 1½ hours in Pullman before leaving for Missoula, Montana where she attends the University of Montana. It is 280 miles from Pullman to Missoula. Shannon stopped for 45 minutes in Wallace, Idaho for dinner. In actual driving time Shannon and Scott averaged 65 mph between Castle Rock and Pullman. Shannon averaged 70 mph between Pullman and Missoula. Castle Rock and Pullman are in the Pacific Time Zone where as Wallace and Missoula are in the Mountain Time Zone.

PROBLEM #14
It took Shannon and Scott two hours to drive the 130 miles from Castle Rock to Boardman, Oregon. Boardman is before lunch in Pasco. If they average the same speed, what time will they arrive in Pullman?
    A. 11:45 AM   B. 12:15 PM   C. 11:30 AM   D. 12:45 PM

PROBLEM #15
If Scott drove 3 out of every five miles from Castle Rock to Pullman, how many miles did Scott drive? How many miles did Shannon drive?
    A. Scott 125; Shannon 200   B. Scott 195; Shannon 130
    C. Scott 200; Shannon 125   D. Scott 130; Shannon 195

PROBLEM #16
It is 142 miles from Pullman to Wallace, Idaho. About what time did Shannon get to Wallace?
    A. 5:15 PM   B. 3:45 PM   C. 4:45 PM   D. 4:15 PM

PROBLEM #17
What time did Shannon arrive in Missoula?
    A. 5:30 PM   B. 8:00 PM   C. 5:45 PM   D. 6:15 PM

PROBLEM #18
How many total miles did Shannon drive?
    A. 410   B. 475   C. 605   D. 272

WARMUPS

1. 16.2 - 30   4. .4 ÷ 25   7. 20% of $45.00?   9. 2^5
2. 16.2 - 3   5. 7 1/3 × 9/11   8. 5/8 – 1/4   10. $\sqrt{49}$
3. 16.2 - .3   6. 5 ÷ 2/3

SOLVE THE FOLLOWING PROPORTIONS:

11. 30 / 24 = U / 32   **12.** 26 / C = 39 / 33   **13.** 45 / 27 = 20 / L

PROBLEM # 14

Three out of every five mullet Jeanette catches in the Gulf of Mexico near Port Arthur, are too small to keep. Last May, she kept sixty mullet. How many mullet did she catch? How many did Jeanette throw back?

    A. 150 caught, 90 thrown back.   C. 100 caught, 60 thrown back.

    B. 150 caught, 60 thrown back.   D. 100 caught, 40 thrown back.

PROBLEM # 15

Three out of every eight Texas Tech football players are from the plains of west Texas. If Texas Tech has 96 football players, how many are from the plains of west Texas? How many are from somewhere else?

A. 24 west Texas, 72 somewhere else.   C. 36 west Texas, 60 somewhere else.

B. 30 west Texas, 66 somewhere else.   D. 36 west Texas, 36 somewhere else.

PROBLEM # 16

Edgar from El Paso saves $2.00 out of every $9.00 he makes at Mike's Minit Mart for college. Last year, Edgar saved $2,430.00 for college. How much money did he make last year? How much money did Edgar spend?

    A. made $27,000; spent $4,860   C. made $19,350: spent $2,150

    B. made $10,935; spent $8,505   D. made $9,870: spent $7440

PROBLEM # 17

Mitch and Bev drove the 770 miles from El Paso to Missouri City. Mitch drove three out of every four miles. How many miles did Mitch drive? How many miles did Bev drive?

A. Mitch 593 miles, Bev 179 miles   C. Mitch 565 miles, Bev 277 miles

B. Mitch 495 miles, Bev 207 miles   D. Mitch 577.5 miles, Bev 192.5 miles

PROBLEM # 18

Old Joe H. from Baycliff usually makes five out of every eight free throws he shoots in the over 50 years old basketball league. Last season Joe shot 56 free throws. How many did Joe miss? How many did he make?

    A. 32 missed, 24 made   C. 35 missed, 21 made

    B. 24 missed, 32 made   D. 21 missed, 35 made

LESSON # 40   PROPORTIONS

WARMUPS
1. 28.2 – 6
2. 28.2 – 60
3. 24 + -15
4. 24 – (-15)
5. -100 ÷ -5 ÷ 2
6. 40% of $75.85
7. 5/8 × 2 1/2
8. 7 1/4
   −5 2/3
9. 5^3
10. $\sqrt{625}$

SOLVE THE FOLLOWING PROPORTIONS:
11. 16 / 18 = W / 45   12. A / 8 = 9 / 6   13. .008 / 6 = 4 / H

PROBLEM # 14
Lath and Gladys drove the 144 miles from El Paso to Van Horn in two hours. If they drive at the same speed, how long will it take them to drive the 360 miles from Van Horn to Tulia?
A. 4 hours   B. 4 ½ hours   C. 5 hours   D. 6 hours

PROBLEM #15
Lath drove four out of every seven miles on their 504 mile trip from El Paso to Tulia. Gladys drove the rest. How many miles did Lath drive? How many miles did Gladys drive?
A. Lath 360 miles, Gladys 144 miles.   B. Lath 288 miles, Gladys 216 miles.
C. Lath 378 miles, Gladys 126 miles.   D. Lath 302 miles, Gladys 202 miles.

PROBLEM #16
Lath and Gladys get approximately 22 miles per gallon of gas in their new car. About how many gallons of gas do they need to drive the 504 miles from El Paso to Tulia? If gas costs $1.40 a gallon, about how much will they spend on gas this trip?
A. 23 gallons of gas, $34.00   B. 23 gallons of gas, $32.00
C. 26 gallons of gas, $36.00   d. 26 gallons of gas, $39.00

PROBLEM #17
Ground beef at Kjallin's Market in Killeen sells at 3 pounds for $5.31. Patty needs seven pounds of ground beef to make tacos for her whole family. How much will it cost her for ground beef?
A. $10.62   B. $11.38   C. $11.94   D. $12.39

PROBLEM #18
The O'Farrell twosome loses 11 golf balls every three rounds of golf they play together. Last summer while playing golf in the same group, Tim O'Farrell lost sixty-one golf balls and Sean O'Farrell lost 82 golf balls. How many rounds of golf did the O'Farrell's play together last summer?
   A. 13 rounds of golf   B.   27 rounds of golf.
   C. 33 rounds of golf.   D.   39 rounds of golf.

(40)

LESSON #41   PROPORTIONS

WARMUPS

1. 24.9 – 6
2. 24.9 – 60
3. 24.9 – .6
4. 4½ × ⅔
5. 8½ – 3⅔
6. 40 ÷ .005
7. -6 + -5 – (-11)
8. -2 × -5 × -4
9. 7^3
10. $\sqrt{196}$

PROPORTIONS

11. $8 / T = 10 / 35$ **12.** $24 / 40 = I / 44$ **13.** $6 / .8 = .9 / M$

PROBLEM #14

Ken and Kathy drove the 268 miles from Longview to Grant's Pass in four hours. If they drive at the same rate, how long will it take them to drive the three hundred thirty-five miles from Grants Pass to Sacramento? If Kathy drove 175 miles from Longview to Sacramento, how many miles did Ken drive?

     A. 5 hours; 428 miles.   B. 4½ hours; 328 miles.
     C. 4 hours; 428 miles.   D. 4 hours;   328 miles.

PROBLEM #15

Josh misses two math problems out of every nine he does at Sabine Middle School in Orange. If Josh missed fourteen problems on the test last week, how many problems were on the test? How many problems did Josh get right?

     A. 63 problems; 49 right.   B. 60 problems; 46 right:
     C. 70 problems; 56 right.   D. 56 problems; 42 right.

PROBLEM #16

Top Flite golf balls sell three for $5.40. Mr. LaBerge from Lake Charles bought three dozen. How much did Mr. LaBerge pay for the golf balls? If he gave six to Mr. Fitts and lost seven last week, how many does he have left?

     A. $64.80; 26 left.   B. $64.80; 23 left.   C. $54.20; 26 left.   D. $54.20; 23 left.

PROBLEM #17

Mr. T makes a math mistake one school day out of every fifteen. If there have been 135 school days so far, how many mistakes has Mr. T made? How many school days did he not make a mistake?

     A. 9 mistakes, 117 days: B. 13 mistakes, 122 days:
     C. 9 mistakes, 126 days: D. 13 mistakes, 112 days :

PROBLEM #18   Steve and Terri drove the 272 miles from Castle Rock

to Cheney in four hours. It took them 12 hours to drive from Castle Rock to Monterey. If they drove at the same rate, how many miles is it from Castle Rock to Monterey? If Steve drove 245 miles on the way to Monterey, how many did Terri drive?

     A. 735 miles;   Terri drove 490 miles.   B. 816 miles;   Terri drove 490 miles.
     C. 735 miles;   Terri drove 571 miles.   D. 816 miles;   Terri drove 571 miles.

LESSON #42   **PROPORTIONS**
WARMUPS
1. $61.4 - 7$ 4. ¾ × $28   7. $5\frac{1}{3} \times 2\frac{1}{4}$ 9. 2^5
2. $61.4 - 70$ 5. $8 - 2\frac{2}{3}$ 8. $15 \div .003$ 10. $\sqrt{64}$
3. $61.4 + 7.77$ 6. 75% of $28

SOLVE THE FOLLOWING:
11. $9 / 24 = T / 16$ 12. $30 / 25 = 18 / I$ 13. $3 / M = .005 / 7$
PROBLEM #14
Elsie eats four out of every five desserts purchased by the Freerks family of Ft. Worth. John and Janet split the rest evenly. If the Freerks family purchased 40 desserts in October, how many did Elsie eat? How many did John eat?
   A. Elsie 32; John 8.   B. Elsie 32; John 4.
   C. Elsie 36; John 4.   D. Elsie 36; John 2.
PROBLEM #15
Mick LaBerge of Lockney makes five out of every eight free throws he attempts. Last month, Mick made 35 free throws. How many did he shoot? How many did he miss?
   A. 50 attempted; 15 missed.   B. 56 attempted; 21 missed.
   C. 45 attempted; 10 missed.   D. 60 attempted; 25 missed.
PROBLEM #16
Mike Shepp's "GRANDE TACO CASA" in McAllen sold 144 beef tacos last Cinco De Mayo. Four out of every nine tacos Mike sells are beef, three out of nine are chicken, and the rest are fish. How many tacos did Mike's "GRANDE TACO CASA" sell last Cinco De Mayo? How many of these tacos were chicken? How many were fish?
A. 324 tacos; 108 chicken; 72 fish.   B. 243 tacos; 75 chicken; 60 fish.
C. 225 tacos;   75 chicken; 50 fish.   D. 225 tacos; 70 chicken; 55 fish.
PROBLEM #17
Lisa of Fibreville spent $18.00 on Walla Walla sweet onions for her brothers Kurt of Big Sandy and Mark of San Marcos. If Walla Walla sweet onions cost 25 pounds for $10.00, how many pounds of onions did Lisa send to her brothers? If Kurt got two thirds of the onions, how many pounds did he get? How many pounds of onions did Mark get?
A. 54 lbs; Kurt 36 lbs; Mark 18 lbs. B. 54 lbs; Kurt 30 lbs; Mark 24 lbs.
C. 45 lbs; Kurt 27 lbs; Mark 18 lbs   D. 45 lbs; Kurt 30 lbs; Mark 15 lbs.
PROBLEM #18
Four out of every seven pitches thrown by Nolan R. of Dallas are fastballs, two out of seven are curves, and the rest are change ups. Last Tuesday, Nolan threw 105 pitches against the Mariners. How many pitches were: fastballs? curves? changeups?
A. 60 fastballs; 35 curves; 10 changeups.
B. 60 fastballs; 30 curves; 15 changeups.
C. 54 fastballs; 36 curves; 15 changeups
D. 54 fastballs; 27 curves; 24 changeups.

LESSON #43   RATIOS & PROPORTIONS
WARMUPS
1. 26.3 – 5   4. 26.3 + 5   7. 3/4 × $28   9. √4/25
2. 26.3 – .5   5. 4 1/5 × 2 1/7   8. $75.45   10. (2/5)³
3. 26.3 – 50   6. .35 ÷ 50   ×   .08
SOLVE THE FOLLOWING PROPORTIONS.
11. 60 / 25 = 48 / T   **12.** 40 / .008 = I / 6   **13.** ¾ / 12 = 9 / M
PROBLEM #14
   Harry and Ardene drove the 420 miles from Longview to Weed in six hours. If
they drive at the same rate, how long will it take them to drive the 630 miles from
Weed to Los Angeles? If Ardene drove 1/4 of the way from Longview to Weed
and 2/5ths of the way from Weed to Los Angeles, how many total miles did Ardene
drive from Longview to Los Angeles? How many total miles did Harry drive?
 A. 9 hours; 357 miles; 693 miles. B. 9 hours; 693 miles; 357 miles.
 C. 8 hours; 262 miles; 788 miles. D. 8 hours; 788 miles; 262 miles.
PROBLEM #15
   Using Harry and Ardene from problem #14, how many miles did Harry drive
from Longview to Weed? From Weed to Los Angeles? How many miles did
Ardene drive from Longview to Weed? From Weed to Los Angeles?
 Harry's Miles   A 105; 157   B 315; 473   C 315; 378   D. 105; 252
 Ardene's Miles   315; 473   105; 157   105; 252   315; 378
PROBLEM #16
   Al's Pro Shop in Amarillo had their big "2/5ths OFF SALE" last week. You
save $2.00 on each $5.00 you spend. Carol bought her husband Ken a golf club
for St. Patrick's Day. If the original price of the club was $85, how much
money did Carol save?   How much did she pay for the golf club?
A. $17; $68.   B. $20; $65.   C. $25; $60.   D. $34; $51.
PROBLEM #17
   Three out of every eight students at Monticello Middle School prefer "wiener
wrap" as their favorite lunch from the cafeteria. One half of the students prefer
"pizza". The rest named "sandwich bar" as their favorite lunch. If there are
960 students that eat in the cafeteria at Monticello Middle School, how many
prefer: 1. wiener wrap? 2. pizza? 3. sandwich bar?
 A. 380; 490; 90. B. 350; 460; 150. C. 300; 480; 180. D. 360; 480; 120.
PROBLEM #18
   Houston has 144 days over 90 degrees F. One sixteenth of them happen in
April, one twelfth happen in May, one sixth in June, five twenty-fourths are
in July, three sixteenths are in August, one eighth in September, one ninth
in October, and the rest are scattered the rest of the year. Find the number
of days Houston has over 90 degrees for April? May? June? July? August?
September? October? The rest of the year?

	April	May	June	July	August	Sept.	Oct.	The Rest
A.	9	12	24	30	27	18	16	8
B.	9	12	24	27	24	21	16	12
C.	6	18	20	30	27	21	15	8
D.	6	18	20	27	24	18	15	16

LESSON #44   **RATIOS & PROPORTIONS**

WARMUPS
1. 32.7 – 8   4. .08 ÷ 40   7. 5 3/5 × 1 1/4   9. 2^6
2. 32.7 – .8   5. 40 ÷ .08   8. $20 ÷ 2/5   10. $\sqrt{64}$
3. 32.7 – 80   6. 4 – 2 1/3

SOLVE THE FOLLOWING:
11. 9T - 18 = 2T + 24   **12.** 12 / 15 = 48 / N   **13.** What is the perimeter and area of a rectangle 15 ft. by 20 ft.?

PROBLEM #14
 Last June, Farmer Byerly harvested four out of every seven rows of Walla Walla sweet onions he planted on his farm in Touchet, Washington. His wife, Maryann, harvested two out of every seven rows. The rest were harvested by Mike or Annie. If Farmer Byerly planted 91 rows of Walla Walla sweet onions, how many rows did he harvest himself? How many rows did Maryann harvest? If Annie harvested three more rows than Mike, how many rows did Annie harvest? How many rows did Mike harvest?
 A. 52; 26; 9; 6. B. 52; 26; 8; 5. C. 48; 24; 11; 8. D. 48; 24; 10; 7.

PROBLEM #15
 At 8:00 am; in March, April, and May; twenty out of every twenty-three days the fairways on Goose Creek Golf Course in Baytown are wet with dew. If this ratio holds next year, how many days in March, April, and May will Goose Creek's fairways have dew at 8:00am? How many days will the fairways not have dew?
 A. 80 days; 12 days. B. 75 days; 17 days. C. 72 days; 20 days. D. 84 days; 8 days.

PROBLEM #16
 Last Thursday, three out of every five of Miss Franette's Algebra I class got either an"A" or a "B" on the chapter 13 test. If there are thirty students in Miss Franette's Algebra I class, how many got either an "A" or a "B"? How many got lower than and "A" or a "B"? If twice as many students got "B's" as got "A's", how many students got an "A" on the test?
 A. 18; 12; 12. B. 18; 12; 6.   C. 24; 6; 8.   D. 24; 6; 16.

PROBLEM #17
 One hundred four paying customers at Connie's Coffee Shop in Seattle paid with cash yesterday. This was four out of every seven paying customers. Two out of every seven paying customers paid with a credit card and the rest paid with check. How many paying customers did Connie's Coffee Shop have yesterday? How many paid with a credit card? How many paid with a check?
 A. 175; 50; 21. B. 182; 60; 18. C. 182; 52; 26. D. 175; 47; 24.

PROBLEM #18
 There are 45 prospective jurors in each group called in Cowlitz County Superior Court. Usually one third of these jurors are excused from jury duty for employment reasons. Two out of every nine are excused for personal knowledge or personal beliefs. The rest form the pool of jurors for a trial. Find the number of prospective jurors that: 1. Are excused for employment reasons. 2. Are excused for personal reasons. 3. Form the jury pool.
 A. 15; 10; 20.   B. 15; 5; 25.   C. 12; 9; 24.   D. 12; 5; 28.

LESSON #45   PROPORTIONS
WARMUPS
1. $35 − $3.55   4. .6 ÷ 12   7. 24 ÷ ⅔   9. $(-3)^3$
2. 12.5 − 8   5. 12 ÷ .6   8. 75% of $52?   10. $\sqrt{169}$
3. 12.5 − 80   6. ¾ × $52

SOLVE THE FOLLOWING PROPORTIONS:
11. 24 / 36 = **T** / 48   **12.** 5 / **I** = 12.5 / 30   **13.** 9 / 12 = 6 / **M**

PROBLEM #14
Lauren got seven out of eight questions correct on Mr. W's first test. If she got 42 questions right, how many questions were on the test?

A. 36   B. 50   C. 48   D. None - Mr W lost the test.

PROBLEM #15
In the 3rd quarter, Katie got a score of five, (the best score possible on homework), on twelve out of every thirteen assignments in Mrs. H's first period class. The rest of the assignments she did not finish and had to copy Zack's assignments. On these she got scores of three or four. If Katie had 48 assignments with a score of five, how many total assignments were there? How many assignments did she copy from Zack?
A. 50 total; 2 copied. B. 52 total; 4 copied. C. 60 total; 12 copied. D. 55 total; 7 copied.

PROBLEM #16
Five out of every seven days during February, Mr. Trinkle played golf. Three out of every four of these rounds of golf were played at The Longview Country Club. Three out of every five of the rounds not played at The Longview Country Club were played at Bandon Dunes and the rest at Gearhart. Find: How many rounds of golf Mr. Trinkle played in February? How many of these rounds were at: The Longview Country Club? Bandon Dunes? Gearhart?
A. 20; 12; 6; 2.   B. 20; 15; 3; 2.   C. 24; 18; 4; 2.   D. 24; 15; 6; 3.

PROBLEM #17
Nick got two more points on Mrs. H's first test than Ariel, three more points than Morgan, but two less points than Francesca. Nick got twelve out of every thirteen points correct on this test. If there were 104 total points on Mrs. Hill's first test, find these student's scores. 1. Nick 2 Ariel 3. Morgan 4. Francesca

A. 96, 98, 99, 93: B. 90, 88, 87, 92: C. 90, 92, 93, 88: D. 96, 94, 93, 98:

PROBLEM #18
During the last fortnight of January, there were 10 hours of coffee time logged in at the teachers table in front of Mr. AW's room. Mr. AW accounted for one of every three of the minutes himself. Mr. CW accounted for two out of every five minutes at the table. Miss F, who spent a lot of time on the internet ordering UCLA BEARWEAR, only logged one out of every twenty minutes at the table. The remaining minutes were split evenly between Mr. K and Mrs. J. Find the number of minutes each of the five teachers spent at the teacher's coffee table in front of Mr. AW's Room the last fortnight of January.

	Mr. AW	Mr. CW	Miss F	Mr. K	Mrs. J
A.	200 minutes	240 minutes	60 minutes	50 minutes	50 minutes
B.	200 minutes	240 minutes,	30 minutes,	65 minutes,	65 minutes
C.	200 minutes	250 minutes	30 minutes	60 minutes	60 minutes
D.	240 minutes	200 minutes	0 minutes	80 minutes	80 minutes

WARM UPS
1. $36.1 - 7$ 4. $-2 -(-9) + -7$ 7. $9\frac{1}{3} - 6\frac{1}{2}$ 9. $(\frac{2}{3})^3$
2. $36.1 - 70$ 5. $10 \times -4 \div .8$ 8. $.8 \div .004$ 10. $\sqrt{.81}$
3. $-8 + -5 -(-13)$ 6. $7 \, 1/2 \div 15/16$

SOLVE THE FOLLOWING:
11. $18 / 40 = 27 / U$ **12.** $C / 24 = 15 / 20$ **13.** $.15 / L = 2.4 / 40$

PROBLEM #14
Jessica got 66 points correct on Mr. Firth's math test. This was 75% correct. How many points were on Mr. Firth's test? How many points did Jessica miss?
    A. 100 points; Jessica missed 34.   B. 100 points; Jessica missed 12
    C. 88 pointst; Jessica missed 22.   D. 88 points; Jessica missed 32

PROBLEM #15
Mr. T and Mrs. T drove the eight hundred miles from Longview to Santa Barbara. Mr. T drove sixty-five percent of the way. How many miles did Mr. T drive? How many miles did Mrs. T drive?
    A. Mr. T 520 mi.;   Mrs. T 380 mi.   B. Mr. T 520 mi.;   Mrs. T 280 mi.
    C. Mr. T 480 mi.;   Mrs. T 320 mi.   D. Mr. T 480 mi.;   Mrs. T 480 mi.

PROBLEM #16
Whitney's mom bought a pizza at Josh's pizza parlor in Lubbock. Being fairly old, Whitney's mom got a senior's discount of 25%. The regular price of the pizza was $18.40. How much did Whitney's mom save on the pizza? How much did she pay for the pizza?
    A. $3.60; paid $14.80.   B. $4.20; paid $14.40.
    C. $5.40; paid $13.00.   D. $4.60; paid $13.80

PROBLEM #17
Dave, a very erratic golfer from Taylorville, saved $120.00 on a new set of golf irons he bought at the Knight Golf Shop in Brownsville. This was a forty percent savings. What was the original price of the golf irons? How much did Dave pay for the golf irons?
    A. $300.00; paid $180.00.   B. $320.00; paid $200.00.
    C. $360.00; paid $240.00.   D. $400.00; paid $280.00

PROBLEM #18
The Seattle Mariners have won forty-eight games so far this year. This is an eighty percent winning record. How many games have the Mariners played this year? How many games have the Mariners lost this year.
    A. played 56 games; lost 8 games.   B. played 60 games; lost 12 games.
    C. played 64 games; lost 16 games.   D. played 72 games; lost 24 games.

WARMUPS
1. $16.3 - 7$ 4. $7\frac{1}{4}$ 6. $60.50   8. $-7 + -9 - (-16)$
2. $16.3 - 70$ $-\ 4\frac{2}{3}$ $\times\ \ .04$ 9. $(1/3)^3$
3. $5/8 \div 1/2$ 5. $.004 \div 8$ 7. 80% of $60.50   10. $\sqrt{9/36}$

SOLVE THE FOLLOWING PROPORTIONS:
11. $24 / T = 60 / 100$ **12.** $51 / 85 = I / 100$ **13.** $21 / 28 = 36 / M$

PROBLEM #14
Jera got 75% on Mr. T's math test. If there were sixty problems on the test, how many problems did Jera get correct? How many problems did she miss?
   A. 40 problems right; missed 20.   B. 50 problems right; missed 10.
   C. 45 problems right; missed 15.   D. 48 problems right; missed 12.

PROBLEM #15
Ronnie and Barbara drove the 600 miles from Longview to Sacramento. If Ronnie drove 60% of the time, how many miles did he drive? How many miles did Barbara drive?
A. Ronnie 320 mi.; Barbara 280 mi.   B. Ronnie 320 mi.; Barbara 240 mi.
C Ronnie 360 mi.; Barbara 340 mi.   D. Ronnie 360 mi.; Barbara 240 mi.

PROBLEM #16
Stacey got 45 points right on Miss Stephanie's 7th grade math test at Lervik Middle School in Lockhart. This score was 90% correct. How many points were possible on the math test? How many points did Stacey miss?
 A. 60 points; Stacie missed 15 points. B. 50 points; Stacie missed 5 points.
 C. 50 points; Stacie missed 15 points. D. 55 points; Stacie missed 10 points.

PROBLEM #17
Marty saved $20.00 on some dandelions for his girl friend Theresa. This was a twenty-five percent savings. What was the regular price of the dandelions? What did Marty pay for Theresa's dandelions?
A. $92.00; Marty paid $72.00   B. $92.00; Marty paid $60.00
C. $80.00; Marty paid $72.00   D. $80.00; Marty paid $60.00

PROBLEM #18
Ryan Campbell from Corpus makes 90% of his free throws. He made 54 free throws last season. How many free throws did Ryan shoot last season? How many did he miss?
   A. Ryan shot 60 free throws; He missed 6.
   B. Ryan shot 60 free throws; He missed 8.
   C. Ryan shot 64 free throws; He missed 10.
   D. Ryan shot 64 free throws; He missed 8.

LESSON # 48   **PROPORTIONS WITH PERCENTS**
WARMUPS

1. $18.3 - 7$ 4. $\$60.55$ 6. $6 \div .003$ 9. $(1/4)^3$
2. $18.3 - 70$ $\quad \times\ .08$ 7. $8 - 3\ 7/8$ 10. $\sqrt{9/36}$
3. $18.3 - .7$ 5. $3/4 \div 1\ 1/2$ 8. 20% of $\$30$

SOLVE THE FOLLOWING PROPORTIONS

11.. $36 / N = 90 / 60$ **12.** $N / 6 = 9 / ¾$ **13.** $.005 / 3 = 4 / N$

PROBLEM #14

Keoke, (the smartest student in his row), got 23 problems right on Mr. Selby's last math test. This was 92% correct. Keoke beat Kristen M. by one problem on the test. Kristen M. beat Katie C. by two problems on the test. Find: 1. How many problems were on the test? 2. How many problems Kristen M missed on the test? 3. How many problems Keoke beat Katie C. by on the test?

A. 25; missed 4; beat Katie by 4.   B 25 ; missed 3; beat Katie by 3.
C. 28; missed 5; beat Katie by 4.   D.28; missed 6; beat Katie by 5.

PROBLEM #15

The Kansas City Royals won 60% of their baseball games last year. If they played 160 games, how many games did they win? How many games did they lose?

  A. 96 wins;   64 losses   B. 90 wins;   70 losses.
  C. 105 wins; 55 losses.   D. 84 wins; 76 losses.

PROBLEM #16

Kelly and Lola drove the 360 miles from San Deigo to Phoenix to watch the Red Devils play baseball. Lola drove 25% of the time. How many miles did Lola drive? How many miles did Kelly drive?

A. 120 miles; 240 miles.   B. 90 miles;   270 miles.
C. 141 miles; 219 miles.   D. 72 miles;   288 miles.

PROBLEM #17

Tim saved forty-six dollars on five "ST SQUARED PUBLISHING" golf shirts at The Longview Country Club Pro Shop. The regular price for five golf shirts is $200.00. What percent discount did Tim get at Jon's Pro Shop? What did Tim pay for the five shirts? What was the sale price for a single shirt?

  A. 23%; $154; $30.80. B. 23%; $150; $30.
  C. 25%; $154; $30.80. D. 25%; $150; $30

PROBLEM #18

Craig from Calvary caught fifty-four sunfish last June in the Toledo Bend Reservoir. This represented 60% of the fish he caught. Thirty percent of the fish Craig caught were catfish. The rest were bass. How many total fish did Craig catch last June? How many catfish did he catch? How many bass did he catch?

  A. 108; 30; 18.   B. 108; 24; 12.   C. 90; 30; 6.   D. 90; 27; 9.

WARMUPS
1. 22.3 – 5   4. -8 × -5 × ½ ÷ 10   7. 25% of $75   9 $(3/7)^2$
2. 22.3 – 50   5. 6 – 3⅔   8. 30 ÷ .0015   10. $\sqrt{9/81}$
3. -11 + -4 – (-15) 6. 5 1/4 × 6/7

SOLVE THE FOLLOWING:
11 24 / N = .2 / .3   12. 76 = 80% of ?   13. 8N + 37 = 13

PROBLEM #14

Mike and Nancy drove the 750 miles from Seattle to Stockton. Nancy drove 60% of the way. How many miles did Nancy drive? How many miles did Mike drive?
  A. 450 miles; 300 miles.   B. 525 miles; 225 miles.
  C. 600 miles; 150 miles.   D. 400 miles; 350 miles.

PROBLEM #15

Scott from Ft. Stockton paid $120.00 for the new graphic version of the Caribbean atlas. This was seventy-five percent of the regular price. What was the regular price of the atlas? How much did Scott save?
A. $160; $40. B. $150; $30. C. $200; $80. D. $144; $24.

PROBLEM #16

Brad and Stephanie drove from Minneapolis to Chicago last month. Brad drove 320 miles which was eighty percent of the trip. Stephanie drove the rest of the way. How many miles is it from Minneapolis to Chicago? How many miles did Stephanie drive?
  A. 360 miles; 40 miles.   B. 400 miles;   80 miles.
  C. 380 miles; 60 miles.   D. 450 miles; 130 miles.

PROBLEM #17

Danielle of Cascade scored 51 points on Mrs. Keith's pre-algebra test. Craig scored six points lower than Danielle on the same test. If Danielle's score was 85% correct, find: 1. How many points were on the test. 2. Craig's points on the test. 3. Craig's percentage correct on the test.
      A. 60; 48; 80%.   B. 60; 45; 75%.
      C. 57; 45; 80%.   D. 57; 48; 75%.

PROBLEM #18

Last May, Walter of Goble caught sixty trout. Forty percent of these were rainbow trout. Three fourths of the remaining trout were cutthroat trout and the rest were brown trout. How many rainbow trout did Walter catch? How many cutthroat trout did he catch? How many brown trout?
A. 24 rainbow;   24 cutthroat;   12 brown.
B. 20 rainbow;   30 cutthroat;   10 brown.
C. 27 rainbow;   24 cutthroat;   9 brown.
D. 24 rainbow;   27 cutthroat;   9 brown.

LESSON #50   PROPORTIONS WITH PERCENTS

WARMUPS

1. $41.3 - 5$
2. $41.3 - 50$
3. $-6 + -5 - (-15)$
4. $-8 \times -5 \div 10$
5. $7 - 3\frac{3}{4}$
6. $6 \frac{1}{4} \div 5/6$
7. 40% of $75?
8. $20 \div .004$
9. $(3/5)^2$
10. $\sqrt{25/36}$

SOLVE THE FOLLOWING:

11. $24/N = 36/27$ 12. $45 = 60\%$ of ?   13. $8N - 37 = 35$

PROBLEM #14

Phil and Nancy drove the 450 miles from Houston to Abilene. Nancy drove 60% of the way. How many miles did Nancy drive? How many miles did Phil drive?
A. 270 miles; 180 miles. B. 288 miles; 192 miles.
C. 320 miles; 160 miles. D. 360 miles; 120 miles.

PROBLEM #15

Danny from Denison paid $60.00 for the new Chinese version of the world atlas for her husband Charles to celebrate Custer's birthday. This was 75% of the regular price. What was the regular price of the atlas? How much did Danny save?
A. $75 ; Danny saved $15. B. $96 ; Danny saved $36.
C. $90 ; Danny saved $30. D. $80 ; Danny saved $20.

PROBLEM #16

Patrick and Amy drove from Houston to New Orleans for Mardi Gras. Patrick drove 252 miles which was seventy percent of the trip. Amy drove the rest of the way. How many miles is it from Houston to New Orleans? How many miles did Amy drive?
A. 360 total mi.; Amy drove 108. B. 400 total mi.; Amy drove 148.
C. 320 total mi.; Amy drove 68. D. 340 total mi.; Amy drove 88.

PROBLEM #17

Johnnie O. of Kelso scored 76 out of 80 points on Mr. Craig's Texas geography test which beat Paula of Trojanville by sixteen points. What percent of the test points did Jonnie O. get correct? What percent did Paula get correct?
A. 90%; 80%. B. 95%; 75%. C. 95%; 80%. D. 90%; 75%.

PROBLEM #18

Katie got 45 problems correct on Ms. Cassie's midterm math test she took on St. Patrick's day at Monticello Middle School in Longview. This gave Katie a score of 90% correct. How many problems were on the test? How many problems did Katie miss? If Emily scored 80% correct on the test, how many problems did Emily get correct?
A. 60 problems; Katie 15; Emily 35. B. 60 problems; Katie 20; Emily 45.
C. 50 problems; Katie 5; Emily 40. D. 50 problems; Katie 5; Emily 35.

LESSON #51   DISCOUNT

WARMUPS

1. $81.7 - 6$
2. $81.7 - 60$
3. $81.7 - .6$

4. 80% of $75
5. $.12 \div 60$
6. $60 \div .12$

7. $3\frac{1}{2} \div 14$
8. $\begin{array}{r} \$75.00 \\ \times \quad .8 \\ \hline \end{array}$

9. $(.3)^3$
10. $\sqrt{.09}$

SOLVE THE FOLLOWING PROBLEMS:

11. $24 / 16 = T / 18$ **12.** $40 / I = .05 / 3$ **13.** $8M + 40 = 16$

SOLVE THE FOLLOWING PROBLEMS:

PROBLEM #14

The regular price of a stereo Colin wants to buy is $250.00. If it is on sale for 20% off, what will his discount be?

   A. $5.00   B. $50.00   C. $125.00   D. $200.00

PROBLEM #15

Winter coats are on sale for 25% off. If the coat that Carolyn wants has a regular price of $80.00, what will her discount be?

   A. $20.00   B. $55.00   C. $60.00   D. $75.00

PROBLEM #16

Video cameras are on sale at Armstrong's Appliances in Edina for 30% off. Kym from Burnsville wants to by a certain video camera to show her Kentucky relatives what "real mosquitoes" look like. If the regular price is $600.00, what will the sale price be?

   A. $180.00   B. 200.00   C. $420.00   D. $582.00

PROBLEM #17

Seth bought a boat on sale for $6,000.00. He received a discount of $2000.00 on the regular price from the Savage Boat Works. What percent discount did Seth receive?

   A. 25%   B. 30%   C. 33⅓%   D. 40%

PROBLEM #18

Tim of Longview bought a new motor scooter at Longview Motor Sports that had a regular price of $2,500.00. Tim's discount was $625.00. What rate of discount did he receive?

   A. 15%   B. 20%   C. 25%   D. 45%

LESSON #52   DISCOUNT

WARMUPS
1. $21.3 - 7$ 4. $-28 \div 4$ 7. 60% of $\$35.25$ 9. 6^3
2. $21.3 - 70$ 5. $5 1/2 \times 3/4$ 8. $2 \div .008$ 10. $\sqrt{100}$
3. $-8 + -5 -(-10)$ 6. $3/8 + 2/3$

SOLVE THE FOLLOWING PROPORTIONS:
11. $25 / 40 = T / 56$ 12. $5 / I = 20 / 28$ 13. $36 / 42 = 24 / M$

Use proportions to solve the following.

PROBLEM #14
Mr. McGuigan bought eighty dollars of crayfish at Terry Dawson's 1980's style fish market in La Porte. Terry always gives a 30% discount an all orders of $80.00 or more. What did Mr. McGuigan pay for the crayfish? How much did he save on this purchase?
  A. $66.00; $24.00   B. $44.00; $36.00
  C. $56.00; $24.00   D. $50.00; $30.00

PROBLEM #15
Mrs. Cutting paid two hundred ten dollars for a new golf driver for her husband Jack. She saved $140.00 off the original price at David Wallace's Golf Shop in Seabrook. What was the original price of the driver? What percent did Mrs. Cutting save?
  A. $350.00; 40%   B. $490.00; 40%
  C. $350.00; 20%   D. $280.00; 20%

PROBLEM #16
Ronnie T. from Evansville bought seven nights at Chet's Double Bogie Motel on South Padre Island for four hundred dollars. The normal price at Chet's Motel for seven days is six hundred dollars. How much money did Ronnie T. save? What percent did he save off the normal price?
  A. $200; 40%   B. $200; 33⅓%   C. $200; 30% D. $100; 25%

PROBLEM #17
Dr. Lucius bought a new computer for his wife at RB'S Computer Outlet in Austin. The regular price of the computer was $880.00. Dr. Lucius got a 25% discount at RB's. How much did Dr. Lucius save? What did he pay for the computer?
  A. $200; $680.00   B. $220; $440.00
  C. $200; $600.00   D. $220; $660.00

PROBLEM #18
Bud Parks from Longview saved $2.40 on Hoya's new golf book, "Two Putting Fast Greens". Bud got a twelve percent discount at the Gap Book Store in Channelview. What was the original price of the book? What did Bud pay for the book?
  A. $20.00; $17.60   B. $200.00; $197.60
  C. $16.00; $13.60   D. $30.00; $27.60

LESSON #53 DISCOUNT
WARMUPS
1. 18.2 − 50
2. 18.2 − 5
3. 18.2 − .5
4. 7 1/2 ÷ 15/16
5. 6 1/2 − 3 3/5
6. .04 ÷ 50
7. $85.75

   × ___.8
8. 80% of $85.75
9. 10^6
10. $\sqrt{.09}$

SOLVE THE FOLLOWING PROPORTIONS
11. 48 / 32 = 9 / T **12.** 8 / 30 = I / 100 **13.** What percent of 60 is 48?

PROBLEM #14
Tony's Pizza Parlor in Tucumcari gives a 25% discount on all classroom pizza parties. Dr. Judy's economics class needs seven large pizzas. The regular price of a Tony's large pizza is $15.00. How much money did Dr. Judy save on the seven pizzas? How much did Dr. Judy actually pay for the seven pizzas?
A. $21.00; $84.00 B. $26.25; $78.75   C. $27.75; $77.25 D. $30.25; $74.75

PROBLEM #15
Wild Bill from Brownsville bought new covers for his sail boat. The covers cost $600.00 at the Ramos Marine Supply Store. Wild Bill got the covers on sale for $510.00. How much money did Wild Bill save on the covers? What percent discount did he get at the Ramos Marine Supply Store?
A. $90.00; 17% B. $90.00; 15% C. $60.00; 10%   D. $60.00; 21%

PROBLEM #16
Delta gives a 15% discount on all airline tickets purchased on their web site. Greg from Grapevine purchased two round trip tickets from Dallas to Atlanta. These round trip tickets normally sell for $180.00 each. How much did Greg save on the tickets by using the web site? What did Greg pay for the two round trip tickets to Atlanta?
A. $54; $324 B. $54; $306   C. $18; $162   D. $72; $288

PROBLEM #17
Terri from Texas City saved $18.00 on the Astros tickets she bought for Saturday's game with the Mariners. Terri paid $72.00 for the tickets. What was the regular price of the tickets? What percent discount did Terri get on the tickets?
A. $90.00; 20%   B. $90.00; 25% C. $84.00; 15% D. $84.00; 25%

PROBLEM #18
Ric's Music Shop in Richardson gives a 20% discount on all historical CD's. Mr. Warren bought the following CD's for his high school history class: Kate Smith's "Over There" Classics ($6.70), Tokyo Rose's Favorite WWII Songs ($7.50), Patty Page's Korean Classics ($8.00), and The Hello Viet Nam Soundtrack ($7.25). How much did Mr. Warren pay for his CD's? How much did Mr. Warren save at Ric's Music Shop?
A. $26.50, $2.95 B. $22.09, $7.36 C. $20.61, $8.84 D. $23.56, $5.89

LESSON # 54   COMMISSION

WARMUPS
1. 26.2 − 4
2. 26.2 − 40
3. 24 ÷ .004
4. .24 ÷ 40
5. 7 − 2 5/6
6. 7 1/2 + 1 2/3
7. -8 + (-5) − (-13)
8. 4 2/3 × 3/7
9. 3^4
10. $\sqrt{36}$

PROPORTIONS
11. $M / 60 = 27 / 45$ 12. $52 / I = 80 / 100$ 13. $18 = 40\%$ of ___?

PROBLEM # 14
Karen Hopper of Sugarland gets a 20% commission on all cell phone systems she sells. She just sold a $400.00 cell phone system to the Gene Smith Catering Company of Kemah. What was Karen's commission?
   A. $50   B. $20   C. $8   D. $80

PROBLEM # 15
Kathy T. of St. Cloud made $135.00 in commissions last week in Amarillo, selling official "Ken Koch Coffee Cups". The Ken Koch company pays fifteen percent commission. How much did Kathy T. sell in Amarillo last week?
   A. $1,350   B. $900   C. $600   D. $2,700

PROBLEM # 16
Darla Morrison of Dallas pays a 24% commission to her sales people on all her hair care products. Her oldest sales person, Diane of Dalhart, sold $2,500 worth of hair care products last December. What was Diane's commission?
   A. $250   B. $100   C. $600   D. $750

PROBLEM # 17
Jackie E. of Big Springs made $255 selling Oregon Duck souvenirs at the Sun Bowl in El Paso last December. The Sun Bowl pays 30% on souvenir sales. What was Jackie's total souvenir sales at the Sun Bowl last December?
   A. $850   B. $2,550   C. $1,020   D. $638.50

PROBLEM # 18
Nelson Carpets of Ft. Worth pays twenty-five percent commission on all carpet sales over $200 and fifteen percent on all carpet sales $200 or less. Last week Carolyn made carpet sales of $1850, $975, $2355, and $160. What was her total commission on these sales?
   A. $1,319   B. $1,274   C. $1,335   D. $1,309

LESSON #55   COMMISSION

WARMUPS
1. 15.92 – 6
2. 15.92 – .6
3. 15.92 – 60
4. $35 ÷ .007
5. 75% of $60
6. 7 1/2 ÷ 15/16
7. 12 – 7 2/3
8. $.35 ÷ 7
9. 5^3
10. $\sqrt{121}$

SOLVE THE FOLLOWING:
11. 8T – 15 = 57   **12.** 12 / 18 = 8 / M   **13.** Find the perimeter and area of a rectangle 15 ft. by 20 ft..

PROBLEM #14
Mykaila works at the Snowmans selling winter sports equipment. She receives an 8% commission on all her equipment sales. Mykaila's sales were $2,000 in December, $3,500 in January, and $2,500 in February. How much commission will she make for the three months?
  A. $64.00   B. $640.00   C. $6,400.00   D. $64,000.00

PROBLEM #15
Cole works for a Toyota dealership in Beaverton. The dealership pays 5% commission on all car sales. Last month; he sold a Tercel for $15,000, 2 Camry's for $20,000 each and a Solara for $25,000. What is Cole's commission for that month?
  A. $400   B. $3,000   C. $4,000   D. $30,000

PROBLEM #16
Anastasia is employed by a real estate agency in Richardson. She gets 4% commission on all her sales of houses. Her commission check this month was $8,000.00. How much were her total sales for the month?
  A. $2,000   B. $3,200   C. $32,000   D. $200,000

PROBLEM #17
Coco from Cooper works at an Moffatt's appliance store in Sulfer Springs. She gets a salary of $500.00 a month plus a 6% commission on all she sells. If she sells $12,000 in appliances this month, what will her total monthly pay be?
  A. $720   B. $1,220   C. $7,700   D. $12,500

PROBLEM #18
Luis works at an insurance agency in McAllen. He receives a 3% commission on all policies he sells. If he sells $50,000 in policies this month, how much commission will he earn?
  A $150.00   B. $1,500.00   C. $15,000.00   D. $50,000.00

(55)

LESSON #56   COMMISSION

WARMUPS
1. $40 – $1.60   4. 8 5/8 – 6   7. $75.00   9. 7^3
2. $40 – $16   5. $75 × ⅔ $\underline{× \ \ .06}$ 10. $\sqrt{169}$
3. $40 – $160   6. $.40 ÷ 8   8. 4¼ – 1⅓

SOLVE THE FOLLOWING PROBLEMS:
11. 6M = 2M + 48   **12.** $24 / A = 75 / 100
13. $36 / $96 = T / 100

PROBLEM #14
Coco from Cooper works at Moffatt's Book Store in Sulfer
Springs. She gets a 12% commission on all her sales. Last month
her book sales (including Practice Practice Practice math books)
totaled $4,500. What was her commission?
    A. $54   B. $540   C. $48   D. $480

PROBLEM #15
Chris just got a job at Video Value. He is given a 7% commission
on all that he sells. In March he sold 3 VCR's for $150.00 each, 6 DVD
players for $125.00 each, and two big screen TV's for $2,500 each.
What was his commission in March?
    A. $194.25   B. $434.00 C. $2,775.00 D. $6,200.00

PROBLEM #16
St. Rose School in Cowlitz County sold magazines for a fundraiser
drive. They got a 20% commission on all the magazines they sold. How
much commission did St. Rose School get if their sales totaled $45,000.00?
    A. $900   B. $2,240   C. $9,000   D. $22,500

PROBLEM #17
Hannah works at Pete's Pet Shop in Port Aransas. She receives a
20% commission on all her sales. If her monthly check for July was
$2,000, how much were her total sales for July?
    A. $400   B. $1,000   C. $4,000   D. $10,000

PROBLEM #18
Sports agent Ian Kretzler just signed the number one pick in the
NBA draft to be a client. Ian receives a 5% commission on whatever
contract his client signs. How much money would the contract have
to be in order for Ian to get a $75,000 commission?
    A. $375,000   B. $1,000,000   C. $1,500,000   D. $2,000,000

WARMUPS

1. 26.7 − 8   4. $55.44   6. 5 1/2 × 8/11   9. 10^5
2. 26.7 − 80   × .06   7. 7 − 3 1/3   10. $\sqrt{1/25}$
3. 26.7 + 8 + 3.3   5. 2 ÷ .04   8. 20% of $850

PROPORTIONS

11. 40 / 12 = E / 9   12. 24 / .018 = 4 / **D**   13. ¾ / **W** = 6 / 24

PROBLEM # 14

Edwardo's Camera Store in Muleshoe gives a 30% discount to all parents of the tennis team for pictures developed during tennis season. Hal W. saved $25.50 last tennis season at Edwardo's. What was the regular price of the pictures Hal bought during tennis season? How much did Hal actually pay for these pictures?
A. $70.50, $44.00   B. $70.50, $45.00   C. $85.00, $60.50   D. $85.00, $59.50

PROBLEM # 15

Fran from Acton gets stuck on her computer two out of every eleven times she turns on her computer. She then has to call Tim (the computer expert) from Texarkana for help. Last week, Fran got stuck and had to call Tim six times. How many times did Fran turn on her computer last week? How many times did Fran turn on her computer and did not have to call Tim?
    A. 33, 27.   B. 33, 31.   C. 30, 24.   D. 66, 60.

PROBLEM # 16

Tom from Temple imports computer software called " Testbanks" from Massachusetts. Tom gives a discount to all schools. Mr. Bradford from Big Sandy paid $105.00 for a $120 regular priced testbank he bought from Tom. How much did Mr. Bradford save? What percent discount did Mr. Bradford get from Tom?
    A. $15 saved, 10% discount   B. $15 saved, 15% discount.
    C. $15 saved, 12½% discount.   D. $15 saved, 17½% discount.

PROBLEM # 17

Five out of every six papers turned into Mr. Trinkle's Pre-Algebra class in Plano are complete. Last week Mr. Trinkle had twenty-five incomplete papers turned in. How many complete papers were turned in to Mr. Trinkle last week? How many total assignments were turned in last week in Mr. Trinkle's class?
    A. 5, 30 total   B. 125, 150 total   C. 25, 150 total   D. 120, 180 total

PROBLEM # 18

Last year in Dallas, 25% of the days in June, July, and August were under 100 degrees. The rest had a high temperature of 100 degrees or more. How many days in June, July, and August were under 100 degrees in Dallas last year? How many days were 100 degrees or more?
A. 30 days, 62 days.   B. 30 days, 60 days.
C. 23 days, 67 days.   D. 23 days, 69 days.

LESSON #58   PROPORTIONS/PERCENT MIXTURE

WARMUPS
1. 31.27 − 4
2. 31.27 − .4
3. 31.27 − 40
4. 20% of $75
5. 4/5 of $75.00
6. .28 ÷ 8
7. 3/4 ÷ 5/6
8. 6 − 2 2/5
9. 5^3
10. $\sqrt{121}$

SOLVE THE FOLLOWING PROPORTIONS:
11. 60/T = 45/21   12. ⅔ / 6 = 8 / M   13. 20 = 80% of ?

PROBLEM #14
Mr. Hopper from Sugarland bought a new set of golf irons at Greatwood Golf Course. The regular price of the irons was $640.00. Cliff, the golf pro, gave Mr. Hopper a 30% discount. How much did Mr. Hopper save on the golf irons? How much did he pay for the irons?
A. $300 saved; $340 paid.   B. $192 saved; $448 paid.
C. $128 saved; $412 paid.   D. $250 saved; $390 paid.

PROBLEM #15
The Texas Rangers have lost three out of every five baseball games since signing their new all-star shortstop. If the Rangers played twenty-five games in May, how many games did they lose? How many games did they win?
A. 10 games lost; 15 games won.   B. 20 games lost;   5 games won.
C. 15 games lost; 10 games won.   D.   5 games lost;   20 games won.

PROBLEM #16
Mr. Estes and Mr. Smith drove the 250 miles from Pasadena to Plano for the Texas Fall BBQ Cook Off. Mr. Smith drove 100 miles. How many miles did Mr. Estes drive? What percent did Mr. Estes drive? What percent did Mr. Smith drive?
A. 100 miles; Estes 50%; Smith 50%   B. 150 miles; Estes 60%; Smith 40%
C. 150 miles; Estes 40%; Smith 60%   D. 150 miles; Estes 55%; Smith 45%

PROBLEM #17
Ricky Ray, director of the Baytown Chamber of Commerce, did a demographic employment study for the city of Baytown. 30% of Baytown's workers work for Exxon, 20% work for the city, county, state or federal government, 10% work for Haliburton, and the rest were too scattered to call. If Baytown has 25,000 employed workers, how many work for: 1. Exxon? 2. The Government? 3. Haliburton?
A. 10,000 Exxon;   5,000 The government;   2,500 Haliburton.
B.   3,000 Exxon;   2,000 The government;   1,000 Haliburton.
C. 10,000 Exxon;   7,500 The government;   5,000 Haliburton.
D.   7,500 Exxon;   5,000 The government;   2,500 Haliburton.

PROBLEM #18
The Twin City Bank in Colorado City pays five percent simple interest on savings accounts. Mr. Jones had $2,500.00 in his savings account on January 1, 2004. He put another $500.00 in his savings account on June 30, 2004. How much interest did Mr. Jones make on his savings in the Twin City Bank in Colorado City for the year 2004?
A. $150.00   B. $137.50   C. $175.00   D. $172.50

LESSON #59   PROPORTION/PERCENT MIXTURE
WARMUPS
1. 24.6 – 5   4. ¾ × $30   6. 7 – 3 5/8   9. 8^3
2. 24.6 – 50   5. $96.75   7. 7 1/2 – 3 5/8   10. $\sqrt{1/36}$
3. $20 – $2.91   × .06   8. 6 2/3 ÷ 5/6

SOLVE THE FOLLOWING PROPORTIONS
11. 10 / K = 35 / 56   12 A / 36 = 35 / 90   13 .12 / 8 = 27 / T

PROBLEM #14
Shane misses three out of every twenty points on Mr. Guglimo's
weekly math tests. The test last Friday was no exception as Shane missed
twelve points. How many points were on Mr. Guglimo's test? How many
points did Shane get correct? If Tad got seventy-one on the test, how many
points did he beat Shane by?

   A. 90, 78, 7.   B. 80, 68, 3.
   C. 90, 75. Tad lost by 4 points.   D. 80, 64, 7.

PROBLEM #15
Trent decided to buy his favorite teacher (Mr. Trinkle by far!!!) some
UCLA golf tees. UCLA golf tees sell for $.84 a dozen. Trent spent
$4.20 for the golf tees. How many UCLA golf tees did Trent buy
for Mr. Trinkle.? How much change did Trent get from a five dollar bill?
A. 60, $.80 change.   B. 60, $.72 change.
C. 72, $.80 change.   D. 72, $.72 change

PROBLEM #16
Mr. Trinkle (problem #15) felt sorry for Mr. Renaud (who only had purple
tees) and Mr. Hadley (who only had crimson tees). Mr. Trinkle kept ½ of the
UCLA golf tees, gave 60% of the rest to Mr. Renaud and what was left over
to Mr. Hadley. How many UCLA golf tees did each person have?
A. Mr. T 60; Mr. R 36; Mr H 24. B. Mr. T 60; Mr. R 40; Mr. H 20.
C. Mr. T. 30; Mr. R 24; Mr. H 6. D. Mr. T 30; Mr. R 18; Mr. H 12.

PROBLEM #17
Searings general store in Beaumont gives a twenty percent discount
to all St. Rose Parish customers. Mark received the St. Rose discount
on a box of "Fancy Dawg Bags" he bought for Rose. These purple and
gold bags can be used instead of wrapping paper for presents. The regular
price for a box of these "Fancy Dawg Bags" is $35.00. How much did Mark
save on these bags? How much did he pay for the bags?
A. $5.00; $30.00.   B. $10.00; $25.00   C. $7.00; $28.00.   D. $7.50; $27.50

PROBLEM #18
Randy and Kathy were driving from Longview, Washington to Missoula,
Montana to take their son David back to college. Kathy drove
forty percent of the time. If it is 490 miles from Longview to Missoula, how
many miles did Kathy drive? Randy drove one third of the remaining miles
and David drove the rest of the time. How many miles did Randy drive?
How many miles did David drive?
 A. 180; 114; 196. B. 196; 180; 114. C. 196; 196; 98. D. 196; 98; 196.

LESSON #60   PROPORTION/PERCENT MIXTURE

WARMUPS
1. 20.45 − 6   4. 5 1/2 × 10/11   7. .006 ÷ 30   9. 7^3
2. 20.45 − 60   5. 8 − 6⅓   8. $60.00   10. $\sqrt{36}$
3. 20.45 − .6   6. 25% of $60.00   <u>×   .25</u>

SOLVE THE FOLLOWING PROPORTIONS
11. 25 / 15 = 45 / T   12. 60 / ¾ = 8 / I   13. .006 / 12 = M / .004

PROBLEM #14
Denny misses two out of every thirteen math problems on Mr. Selby's math tests. If Denny missed 8 problems on the February 24th test, how many problems were on the test? How many problems did Denny get right? Denny (who usually beats Tabitha and Melissa on most math tests) got 5 more problems right than Melissa. How many problems did Melissa get correct on the test?
A. 60; 52; 47.   B. 60; 52; 57.   C. 52; 44; 39.   D. 52; 44; 49.

PROBLEM #15
Longhorn Golf Balls sell for $19.50 a dozen. If Joan buys 48 Longhorn Golf Balls, how much will it cost her? How much change will Joan get back from a hundred dollar bill? If she gives two dozen golf balls to Mr. Trinkle, one half a dozen to Mr. Arveson, and 8 golf balls to Mr. Smith, how many golf balls will she have left?
A. $78.00; $22.00; 10.   B. $76.00; $24.00; 10.
C. $78.00; $22.00; 8.   D. $76.00; $24.00; 8.

PROBLEM #16   David, the smartest student in his row, got 92% on the last math test. If there were 25 problems on the test, how many problems did David get right? How many problems did David get wrong?
A. 23 right; 2 wrong.   B. 2 right; 5 wrong.
C. 22 right; 3 wrong.   D. 18 right; 7 wrong.

PROBLEM #17
Anton tutors for math tests and math homework. Anton is a smart math student and almost never misses math answers. Tyler, who cannot figure out some of the math answers himself, is one of Anton's best customers. Anton gives his good customers, like Tyler and Sam, a 30% discount. Tyler's bill came to $40.00 last January before his discount. How much did Tyler save with his discount? What did Tyler pay for the tutoring? How much change did Tyler get from a $50.00 bill?
A. $16; $24; $26.   B. $12; $28; $22.   C. $10; $30; $20.   D. $ 8; $32; $18.

PROBLEM #18
Megan G. from Galveston went to buy a poster of her favorite band at the mall. When she got to the store, she discovered that they had a twenty-five percent discount on all posters that day. She bought 5 posters, (two of her favorite member, Jesse, and three of the group). If the posters were originally $5.95 each, how much money did Megan save? How much did she pay for the posters? How much change did she get from $25.00?
A. $7.50; $22.50; $2.50.   B. $8.27; $21.73; $3.27.
C. $6.72; $23.23; $1.77.   D. $7.44; $22.31; $2.69.

LESSON #61   PROPORTION/PERCENT MIXTURE

WARMUPS
1. -7 + -21 −(-20)   4. 5/9 ÷ 2 1/4   7. 3/4 × $36   9. 10^4
2. -10 × 5 ÷ -2   5. 9 − 5 7/8   8. 20% of $75.55   10. $\sqrt{400}$
3. 21 − 10.3   6. .06 ÷ 15

SOLVE THE FOLLOWING
11. 12 / U = 30 / 9   12. 8C − 35 = 37   13. 10L + 8 = 3L + 15

PROBLEM #14

Two out of every five faculty members at New Braunfels Jr. High are Texas A&M Aggie fans. There are seven fewer Texas Longhorn fans than Aggie fans on the faculty. The rest of the faculty is too scattered to categorize. If there are sixty faculty members at New Braunfels Jr. High, how many are Texas A&M Aggie fans? How many are Texas Longhorn fans? How many faculty members are neither Aggie nor Longhorn fans?
A. 20 A&M; 13 Tex; 27 other.   B. 24 A&M; 17 Tex; 19 other.
C. 25 A&M; 18 Tex; 17 other.   D. 28 A&M; 21 Tex; 11 other.

PROBLEM #15

Texas Tech Red Raider football season tickets sell at $360 for two seats. If you buy them by May 1st, there is a 25% discount. Andrew from Amarillo purchased two seats on April 16th, (his wedding anniversary), for his wife Weese. How much did Andrew save on the two season tickets? What did Andrew pay?
A. $108; $252.   B. $120; $240.   C. $ 72; $288.   D. $90; $270.

PROBLEM #16

Dan and Laurel drove the 204 miles from Electra to Amarillo in 3 hours. If they drive at the same rate, how long will it take them to drive the 476 miles from Amarillo to Dallas? If Dan drove three out of every four miles, how many miles did Dan drive between Amarillo and Dallas? How many miles did Laurel drive?
A. 7 hr.; 357 mi.; 119 mi.   B. 7 hr.;   360 mi.; 116 mi.
C. 8 hr.; 357 mi.; 119 mi.   D. 8 hr.;   360 mi.; 116 mi.

PROBLEM #17

Denise saved $36 on a new Baylor Bear blanket at "The Bagger Store" in Waco. The Bagger Store gives a 20% discount on all blankets. What was the original price of the Baylor Bear Blanket? What did Denise pay for the blanket?
A. $240; $204.   B. $120; $94.   C. $144; $108.   D. $180; $144.

PROBLEM #18

The Russells of Texarkana had a garage sale. They took in $840.00 at this garage sale. The Russells split the money this way: Larry 1/4, Kathy 3/10, Robyn 1/5, Brandon 3/20, and Lizzie 1/10. How much money did each of the Russells make?
A. Larry $210; Kathy $240; Robyn $180; Brandon $126; Lizzie $84.
B. Larry $196; Kathy $252; Robyn $168; Brandon $140; Lizzie $84.
C. Larry $196; Kathy $240; Robyn $180; Brandon $140; Lizzie $84.
D. Larry $210; Kathy $252; Robyn $168; Brandon $126; Lizzie $84.

LESSON #62   PROPORTION/PERCENT MIXTURE
WARMUPS
1. $17.1 - 30$ 4. $3/4 \times 8/9$ 6. $\$80.45$ 8. $20 \div .0004$
2. $17.1 - 3$ 5. $8 - 2\ 2/3$ $\times\ .07$ 9. $(.2)^3$
3. $17.1 - .3$ 7. 20% of $\$75$ 10. $\sqrt{121}$

SOLVE THE FOLLOWING PROPORTIONS:
11. $12 / N = 8 / 15$ 12. $12 / 15 = N / 100$ 13. $28 = 40\%$ of ?

PROBLEM #14
Alice from Tinglev got 90 emails in January. Eighty percent of these were from Denmark. One third of the remaining emails were from Germany. The rest were from the USA. How many of Alice's emails were from: Denmark? Germany? The USA?
A. 78; 4; 8. B. 60; 12; 18. C. 66; 8; 16. D. 72; 6; 12.

PROBLEM #15
Stanley from Seaside wanted to buy some 2 lb. blocks of Tillamook Cheese to send to his Texas relatives for Bastille Day. Stanley bought two blocks for Patti from Port Arthur, two blocks for cousin Kelly from Kileen, one block for Lola from Lubbock, one block for Ashley from Austin, and two blocks for Kelsey of Kempher. If two pound blocks of Tillamook Cheese sell at three for $15.30, how much did Stanley pay for the cheese to send to his Texas relatives? How much change did he get from a fifty dollar bill?
A. $45.60; $4.40. B. $40.80; $9.20. C. $33.80; $16.20. D. $36.60; $13.40.

PROBLEM #16
Jakob missed eight points on Mr. Christensen's pre-algebra math test at Lake Jackson Middle School. If Jakob got 72 points correct, what percent did Jakob get correct? What percent did Jakob miss?
A. 80%; 20%. B. 85%; 15%. C. 90%; 10%. D. 95%; 5%.

PROBLEM #17
Four out of every seven customers at Soren's Seafood Restaurant and Chowder House in Seabrook prefer fish for their dinner meal, two out of seven choose beef and the rest choose pasta. Last Thursday night Soren's sold fifty-six fish dinners. If the normal dinner ratios hold true, how many customers did Soren's serve Thursday night? How many beef dinners did he serve that night? How many pasta dinners did he serve?
A. 98 customers; 28 beef; 14 pasta. B. 90 customers; 22 beef; 12 pasta.
C. 104 customers; 32 beef; 16 pasta. D. 110 customers; 36 beef; 18 pasta.

PROBLEM #18
Carsten from Jaegerspris lost nine golf balls the first two days of his ten day golf vacation to the Rio Grande Valley. This was 75% of the golf balls he lost on his vacation. How many total golf balls did Carsten lose on his vacation? If golf balls sell three for $8.10, how much did Carsten spend for his lost golf balls?
A. 12; $24.30. B. 15; $32.40. C. 15; $24.30. D. 12; $32.40.

LESSON #63 PROPORTION/ PERCENT MIXTURE

WARMUPS
1. 19.3 − 4
2. 19.3 − 40
3. -7 + -13 − (-6)

4. -8 − 9 − (-21)
5. -5 × -8 ÷ 10
6. 4 1/2 × 2/15

7. 7 1/3
   − 1 3/5
8. 24 ÷ .006

9. 4^3
10. $\sqrt{625}$

SOLVE THE FOLLOWING PROPORTIONS AND EQUATIONS

11. 24 / 30 = 16 / C   **12.** 8W + 43 = 11   **13.** 12M = 2M + 40

PROBLEM #14
Craig and Melanie from Albion drove the 288 miles from Detroit to Chicago in four hours. If they drive at the same rate, how long will it take them to drive the nine hundred thirty-six miles from Chicago to Dallas?
   A.   9 hours.   B. 12 hours.   C. 13 hours.   D. 15 hours.

PROBLEM #15
Craig (problem #14) drove 25% of the way from Detroit to Chicago and 75% of the way from Chicago to Dallas. How many miles did Craig drive from Detroit to Chicago? From Chicago to Dallas?
A. 72 mi.: 702 mi. B. 72 mi.; 668 mi. C. 96 mi.; 702 mi. D. 96 mi.; 668 mi.

PROBLEM #16
Kayla from Kima has fifty-four CD's. This is 60% of her family's total CDs. Kayla's brother Corbin has two thirds of the remaining CD's. The rest belong to Kayla's parents. How many total CD's does Kayla's family have? How many CD's belong to Corbin? How many belong to Kayla's parents?
 A. total 96; Corbin 28; parents 14.   B. total 96; Corbin 30;   parents 12.
 C. total 90; Corbin 27; parents 9.   D. total 90; Corbin 24;   parents 12.

PROBLEM #17
Gerry of Paris, Texas rented an apartment in Paris, France for the month of October. Gerry rented it from Stella's European Rentals of San Antonio. Gerry got a 40% discount off the $2,160.00 regular price from Stella's Rentals. How much money did Gerry save? What did Gerry pay for the apartment?
 A. $540; $1,620. B. $864; $1,296. C. $432; $1,728. D. $640; $1520.

PROBLEM #18
Last football season Kevin B. of Brownsville got three out of every five football predictions correct in September, four out of every seven correct in October, and two out of every five correct in November. If Kevin made forty-five predictions in September, forty-nine predictions in October and sixty predictions in November, how many predictions did he get correct last football season? How many predictions did Kevin miss?
A. 84; 70.   B. 79; 75.   C. 72; 82.   D. 90; 64.

LESSON #64   PROPORTION/PERCENT MIXTURE

WARMUPS
1. $26.3 - 7$ 4. $\$70 + \$23.57 + \$1.43$ 7. $24 \div .06$ 9. 2^4
2. $26.3 - .7$ 5. 25% of $\$36 = ?$ 8. $.24 \div 6$ 10. $\sqrt{81}$
3. $26.3 - 70$ 6. $\frac{3}{4}$ of $\$36$

SOLVE THE FOLLOWING PROPORTIONS AND EQUATIONS
11. $24/36 = 60/B$ 12. $15/T = 9/12$ 13. $6M - 17 = 25$

Two fifths of the boys and one third of the girls in Miss B's 6th period English class at Longview High School were ready to give their speech the first day the speeches were due. Five eighths of Miss B's 6th period class are boys. If there are sixteen students in Miss B's 6th period class, FIND:

PROBLEM #14
   1. How many boys are in the class?   2. How many girls are in the class?
   3. How many girls were ready to give their speeches the first day?
 A. 12 boys: 4 girls; 1 girl ready.   B. 12 boys: 4 girls: 2 girls ready.
 C. 10 boys: 6 girls; 2 girls ready.   D. 10 boys: 6 girls: 4 girls ready.

PROBLEM #15
   1. How many boys were ready to give their speeches the first day.
   2. How many girls were not ready to give their speeches the first day?
   3. How many students were not ready to give their speeches the first day?
A. 4 boys; 4 girls; 10 not ready.   B. 4 boys; 6 girls; 10 not ready.
C. 6 boys; 2 girls; 8 not ready.   D. 6 boys; 4 girls; 8 not ready.

PROBLEM #16
   1. What percent of Miss B's 6th period class are boys? 2. What percent of Miss B's 6th period class are girls? 3. What percent of Miss B's 6th period class were not ready with their speeches the first day?
A. 60% boys;   40% girls;   62½% not ready.
B. 60% boys;   40% girls;   60% not ready.
C. 62½% boys; 37½% girls;   60% not ready.
D. 62½% boys; 37½% girls;   62½% not ready.

PROBLEM #17
   1. What percent of the boys in Miss B's 6th period class were ready with
      their speeches the first day?   2. What percent of the girls in Miss B's
      6th period class were ready with their speeches the first day?
      A. 40% boys; 30% girls.   B.   40% boys; 33 ⅓% girls.
      C. 60% boys; 33⅓% girls.   D. 60% boys; 30% girls.

PROBLEM #18
The second day the speeches were due there were two more boys and two more girls ready to give their speeches. Find:
   1. What percent of the boys were still not ready to give their speeches?
   2. What percent of the class was still not ready to give their speeches?
A. 60% boys; 33⅓% class. B. 50% boys; 40% class.
C. 40% boys; 37½% class. D. 25% boys; 30% class.

LESSON # 65   PROPORTION/ PERCENT MIXTURE
WARMUPS
1. $25.2 - 40$ 4. $3 1/2 \div 7/8$ 7. 25% of $\$60$?   9. 4^3
2. $25.2 - 4$ 5. $7 1/3 - 5 3/4$ 8. $\$75.40$ 10. $\sqrt{144}$
3. $25.2 \div .4$ 6. $28 \div .007$ $\underline{\times\ .06}$

SOLVE THE FOLLOWING PROPORTIONS AND EQUATIONS
11. $24 / 30 = 60 / T$ 12. $4I + 14 = 42$ 13. $5M = M + 28$

PROBLEM #14
  Caitlin scored fifty-seven points on Mr. Guglimo's Ground Hog Day math test.
Caitlin beat Shane by three points, but lost to Steve by two points. If Caitlin's
score was 95% correct, find: 1. How many points were on the test?
2. Shane's score. 3. Shane's percent correct? 4. Steve's score?
  A. 1. 60; 2. 54; 3. 90%; 4. 59.   B. 1. 60; 2. 54; 3. 90%; 4. 58.
  C. 1. 65; 2. 55; 3. 85%; 4. 58.   D. 1. 65; 2. 55; 3. 92%; 4. 58.

PROBLEM #15
  Braxton, the top student in Mr. Guglimo's math class, is also great at mowing
lawns in record time. Braxton's back yard is a rectangle 150 ft. by 90 ft..
Braxton's mower cuts an 18 inch strip of grass. Braxton can make three 150 ft.
passes in two minutes with his mower. How long will it take Braxton to mow
his back yard? How many square feet are in Braxton's back yard?
  A. 60 min.; 12,000 ft^2 B. 40 m.in; 12,000 ft^2
  C. 60 min.; 13,500 ft^2 D. 40 min.; 13,500 ft^2

PROBLEM #16
  The three best golfers on the Mark Morris High golf team all average over 200
yards on their tee shots. Jesh hits his drives 10% shorter than Jordan, and Shane hits
his 15% farther than Jordan. Shane's dad hits his drives five-sixths as far as Shane.
If Jordan drives the ball 240 yards, find: Jesh's driving distance? Shane's driving
distance? Shane's dad's driving distance?
A. 220 yds; 260 yds; 215 yds.   B. 216 yds; 270 yds; 224 yds.
C. 220 yds; 254 yds; 215 yds.   D. 216 yds; 270 yds; 230 yds.

PROBLEM #17
  Erin bought a pair of new Dr. McIntosh's Sandals at the spring shoe sale in
Brownsville. These particular sandals normally sell for $80.00. However, Erin
got the 35% spring sale discount. How much money did Erin save on the sandals?
How much did Erin pay for the sandals?
A. $20; $60. B. $16; $64. C. $32; $48. D. $28; $52.

PROBLEM #18
  Twenty-three students in Mr. Smith's 1st period class turned in their english paper
on time today. This is 92% of first period. Third period had one more student turn
in their work on time than first period. Fifth period had four less students than third
period turn in their work on time. If all three classes have the same number of students,
how many students are in each class? What percent of the 3rd period students turned
in their work on time? What percent of the fifth period students turned in their work
on time?
  A. 25 students; 3rd 96%; 5th 80%.   B. 25 students; 3rd 96%; 5th 76%.
  C. 27 students; 3rd 95%; 5th 80%.   D. 27 students; 3rd 95%; 5th 76%.

LESSON #66   MONEY

WARMUPS
1. $27.30 − $5
2. $27 − $5.30
3. $27.30 + $8 + $4.70
4. .04 ÷ 50

5. 2/3 × $36
6. 4 1/5 ÷ 1 3/4
7. $70.65
   ×   .8

8. 80% of $70.65
9. 10^5
10. $\sqrt{121}$

SOLVE THE FOLLOWING
11. $25 is what percent of $40?
12. $18 / T = 60 / 100
13. 8M − $24 = $32

PROBLEM #14
Kevin from Pullman was offered a deal to write math story problems for ST^2 Publishing. For every 5 he wrote he would be paid $12.00. How much did Kevin get paid per problem?
    A. $2.00   B. $2.50   C. $2.40   D. $7.00

PROBLEM #15
How much would Kevin get paid for writing 12 problems?
    A. $14.40   B. $28.80   C. $30.00   D. $288.00

PROBLEM #16
As Kevin got better he wanted a raise to $14.00 per 5 problems. How much more per problem was this?
    A. $.40   B. $.50   C. $2.00   D. $.70

PROBLEM #17
After Kevin got his raise he wrote 100 problems. How much more did he make with the raise than he would have made before the raise?
    A. $14.00 $120.00   C. $40.00   D. $50.00

PROBLEM #18
Kevin wanted to buy a subwoofer for his truck. The one he wanted cost $370.00. With his raise to $14.00 for 5 problems, how many problems would he have to write to earn enough for the subwoofer?
    A. 133   B. 1,330   C. 132   D. 155

Think how much
teacher prepartions time
a **classroom set** of
Practice Practice Practice
books will save?????
(66)

LESSON #67 - MONEY

WARMUPS

1. 14.3 − 5
2. 14.3 − 50
3. 14.3 − .5
4. -7 + -9
5. 7 − (-9)
6. 60 ÷ .003
7. 5
$-3 \ 1/7$
8. 4 1/5 ÷ 7/10
9. 4^3
10. $\sqrt{625}$

SOLVE THE FOLLOWING:

11. 36 / T = 30 / 45   12. $28 = ?% of $70.

13. Split $120.00 into these shares. Tim 1/3, Tom 1/2, Steve 1/6

PROBLEM #14

Ben bought ten baseball cards at Rodriguez's Hobby Store in McAllen. Two of Ben's cards cost $.35 each. He bought a three card packet for $1.25. The remaining cards were all $.42 each. Ben gave Mr. Rodriguez a ten dollar bill. What was the total price of Ben's ten baseball cards? How much change did he get back from Mr. Rodriguez?

A. $6.13; $2.87.   B. $3.63; $6.37.   C. $5.05; $4.95.   D. $4.05; $5.95.

PROBLEM #15

Texas tangerines sell 6 for $.51. At Christmas, Tom from Brownsville sent two dozen tangerines to Alex, one dozen to Kevin, three dozen to Kathy, and a dozen to Ed. How much did Tom pay for the tangerines?

A. $3.57   B. $6.12   C. $8.16   D. $7.14

PROBLEM #16

Round trip airline tickets from San Antonio to Orlando are $210.00 each. During the "SPRING BREAK SPECIAL" spouses fly for 75% and children for one half that price. Al from Kirby plans to fly his wife Sherri, son Ben, and daughter Hanna next spring break from San Antonio to Orlando. What will it cost Al to fly his family of four?

A. $577.50   B. $630.00   C. $525.00   D. $672.50

PROBLEM #17

The price of crayfish at Hoyas' Supermarket in Baytown is $8.50 for a 15 pound sack. Marinated rib steaks costs $3.50 a pound at Hoya's. Ricky Ray and Pat from Baytown bought 45 pounds of crayfish and 15 pounds of rib steak for their "Surf & Turf" party. How much will the crayfish and rib steak cost Ricky Ray and Pat?

A. $135.00   B. $ 69.50   C. $ 92.00   D. $ 78.00

PROBLEM #18

The Selbys from San Marcos took in $600.00 on their garage sale. They split the money this way: Steve 1/4, Terri 1/3, Shannon 1/6, Scott 1/8, and Tasha the rest. How much money did each Selby get from the garage sale?

	Steve	Terri	Shannon	Scott	Tasha
A.	$150	$200	$125	$75	$50
B.	$175	$225	$100	$60	$40
C.	$175	$225	$100	$80	$20
D.	$150	$200	$100	$75	$75

LESSON #68   MONEY

WARMUPS

1. 21.6 − 3	4. 1 2/3 ÷ 5	7. $91.17	9. 2^5
2. 21.6 − 30	5. 5 − 1 1/8	× .06	10. $\sqrt{121}$
3. 3/5 ÷ 3/4	6. .06 ÷ 20	8. 20 ÷ .05	

SOLVE THE FOLLOWING PROPORTIONS

11. 15 / 20 = 18 / **T**   **12.** 3 / **I** = .004 / 6   **13.** 20 / 5 = **M** / ¾

PROBLEM #14

Pepperoni Sticks sell three for $2.46 at Dae's Minit Mart in Dalhart. Jin bought five pepperoni sticks at Dae's Market. How much did the pepperoni sticks cost Jin? How much change did Jin get from a $5.00 bill?

A. $4.25; $ .75   B. $4.15; $ .85   C. $4.00; $ 1.00   D. $4.10; $ .90

PROBLEM #15

The Hunter Family of Hawdon split the $600.00 they made from their garage sale last week this way: Mike 1/3; Nancy 1/4; Dana 1/5; Scott 1/6; and Brad 1/20. How much of the $600.00 did each family member get?

	Mike	Nancy	Dana	Scott	Brad
A.	$200;	$150;	$120;	$100;	$30.
B.	$175;	$150;	$140;	$120;	$15.
C.	$200;	$125;	$120;	$85;	$70.
D.	$175;	$160;	$140;	$100;	$25.

PROBLEM #16

Roy bought the following items at Connie's Bait & Tackle Shop in Port Lavaca: two containers of shrimp at $3.50 each; 4 dozen worms at $1.70 a dozen; 5 flatfish lures at $2.15 a lure; and 6 sinkers at $.47 each. What was Roy's total bill? How much change did Roy get from a fifty dollar bill?

A. $28.52; $21.48   B. $25.75; $24.25   C. $31.74; $18.26   D. $27.37; $22.63

PROBLEM #17

Ken's Smoked Fish of Kalama sells smoked salmon at $8.52 for 3 cans and smoked sturgeon at 4 cans for $11.56. Betty of Beaumont bought 15 cans of smoked salmon and 20 cans of smoked sturgeon on the internet from Ken's Smoked Fish of Kalama. If the shipping costs were 5%, what was Betty's final bill for this order?

A. $100.40   B. $110.04   C. $105.42   D. $112.42

PROBLEM #18

The Thomas family made $120.00 selling golf balls they found to Katie's Driving Range. The Thomas's found these golf balls in the brush by hole number ten at The Longview Country Club. They split the $120.00 this way: Gene 1/3; Jill 2/5; Riley 1/6; Zak - the money that was left. How much money did each Thomas get from the sale of these golf balls?

	Gene	Jill	Riley	Zak
A.	$40	$48	$24	$ 8
B.	$36	$54	$30	$10
C.	$36	$42	$30	$12
D.	$40	$48	$20	$12

LESSON #69   MONEY

WARMUPS
1. 15.31 − 3
2. 15.31 − .3
3. 15.31 − 30

4. 4 1/2 × 4/9
5. $\begin{array}{r} 8 \\ -\ 2\ 2/3 \end{array}$

6. .8 ÷ .004
7. .004 ÷ 8
8. 20% of $75.25

9. 2^6
10. $\sqrt{169}$

SOLVE THE FOLLOWING:
11. $18 / U = 24 / 44$ 12. $C / 75 = 20 / 100$ 13. $8L = 2L + 42$

PROBLEM #14
Stephanie from McGuigan bought a gallon of Washington apple cider at Tom's Texas Coast Market. Stephanie saved $3.00 off the $7.50 regular price of the apple cider. What percent discount did Stephanie get on the cider? What did she pay for the cider?
A. 40%; $3.50   B. 30%; $3.50   C. 40%; $4.50   D. 30%; $4.50

PROBLEM #15
Mr. Gap of Galveston made $10,500 in insurance commissions selling "Moon Insurance" on the east Texas coast last year. Mr. Gap makes 15% commission on all "Moon Insurance" he sells. How much "Moon Insurance" did Mr. Gap sell last year?
A. $ 21,000   B. $105,000   C. $ 85,000   D. $ 70,000

PROBLEM #16
"Moon Insurance" makes up 12½% of Mr. Gap's (problem #15) total insurance commissions. What are his total insurance commissions?
A. $ 31,500   B. $105,000   C. $ 70,000   D. $84,000

PROBLEM #17
Mr. Scott of Sabine sold a new Tahoe to Mr. Worthington of Waco for $32,500. The Texas sales tax is 7%. How much tax did Mr. Worthington pay on his new Tahoe?
A. $2,240.00   B. $2,275.00   C. $2,315.00   D. $2,455.00

PROBLEM #18
Mr. Scott (problem #17) makes 14% commission on all Tahoe sales before taxes. How much commission did Mr. Scott make on his Tahoe sale to Mr. Worthington?
A. $4,550.00   B. $3,840.00   C. $4,875.00   D. $4,225.00

(**69**)

ST^2 Publishing - 360-636-2645 (st2pub.com - web site) - If any questions, just call or email.

LESSON #70   MONEY
WARMUPS
1. 24.3 − 5   4. 24.3 + 36.5   7. 7 − 6¾   9. 4^3
2. 24.3 − 50   5. 4 1/2 × 6/9   8. $75.55   10. $\sqrt{144}$
3. 24.3 − .5   6. 20 ÷ .005   × .06

SOLVE THE FOLLOWING:
11. T / 28 = 55 / 35   **12.** N / $75 = 40 / 100   **13.** $24 = ?% of $60?

PROBLEM #14

Kevin is the number one salesman for ST2 PUBLISHING in Longview. Kevin's territory is Dallas to Austin to Houston and all parts east to the border. Last month Kevin made $4,800 in commissions. If ST2 PUBLISHING pays 20% commission, how much did Kevin sell last month?
   A. $14,400   B. $19,200   C. $20,000   D. $24,000

PROBLEM #15

Alex of Austin ordered $180 worth of "Cougar Gold Cheese" for Christmas presents. The Washington State University Creamery gives a 15% alumni discount on all "Cougar Gold Cheese". How much did Alex save by being an alumni of Washington State University? How much did Alex pay for the cheese?
   A. $27 saved; $153 paid.   B. $24 saved; $156 paid.
   C. $30 saved; $150 paid.   D. $36 saved; $144 paid.

PROBLEM #16

Greg from Bothel bought 10 Cougar Sun Bowl sweatshirts to take to his friends back home. He bought these at Scott's Sun Bowl Supplies in El Paso. If Cougar Sun Bowl sweatshirts sell three for $156.00, what did Greg pay for the ten sweatshirts?
   A. $540   B. $520   C. $600   D. $515

PROBLEM #17

Sherri from Shreveport spent $108 at the Shreveport Golf Course last week. Two ninths of Sherri's money was spent on golf balls, one third of her money was spent on a golf shirt and the rest was spent on a sweater vest. How much did Sherri spend for golf balls? The golf shirt? The sweater vest?
A. $18 golf balls; $30 shirt; $60 vest. B. $18 golf balls; $36 shirt; $54 vest.
C. $24 golf balls; $30 shirt; $54 vest. D. $24 golf balls; $36 shirt; $48 vest.

PROBLEM #18

Shannon of Castle Rock was going to buy a car at Tasha's used cars in Texarkana. Shannon paid $17,500 for a car plus 7% sales tax and ½% for the extended service contract. How much sales tax did Shannon pay? What did she pay for the extended service contract? What was the total price of the car after the sales tax and the extended service contract were paid?
A. $1,150; $87.50; $18,737.50.   B. $1,150; $93.50; $18,743.50.
C. $1,225; $87.50; $18,812.50.   D. $1,225; $93.50; $18,818.50.

(**70**)

LESSON #71   MONEY

WARMUPS

1. $24 − $1.75   4. $95.75   6. $75 ÷ 50   9. $(⅓)^3$
2. $24.35 − $5   ×   .06   7. 20% of $75   10. $\sqrt{9/36}$
3. $20 ÷ .005   5. 3/4 of $42?   8. 1¾ × $28

SOLVE THE FOLLOWING:

11. $8T = 3T + \$55$ 12. $8I = -3I + \$55$ 13. $M / \$35 = 40 / 100$

PROBLEM #14

Which of the following is the "BEST BUY"?
A. A dozen golf balls for $27?   B. Three golf balls for $6.75?
C. $2.25 per golf ball?   D. A, B, and C are all the same.

PROBLEM #15

John S. of Port Arthur Fish and Marine sold a new boat to Danette of Dallas.
John made $2,430.00 in commission for this sale. If Port Arthur Fish and Marine
pays 18% commission on new boat sales, what did Danette pay for the boat?
A. $ 437.40   B. $15,500.00   C. $10,500.00   D. $13,500.00

PROBLEM #16

Emrich's of Washougal is having a 40% fall close out sale on all their
summer things on September 17th. Pat bought two pairs of shorts at this sale.
She saved $25.60 on his total bill. What was the original price of the two
pairs of shorts? How much did Pat pay for the shorts?
A. $64.00;   Pat paid $38.40   B. $64.00;   Pat paid $19.20.
C. $102.40; Pat paid $76.80   D. $102.40;   Pat paid $51.20.

PROBLEM #17

The Longhorn Classic Basketball Tournament last December split their net
earnings this way: Texas 2/5, Texas A&M 1/3, Arkansas 1/5 and Minnesota the
rest. If the net earnings of the tournament were $90,000, find each schools share
of the $90,000.00.

	Texas	Texas A&M	Arkansas	Minnesota
A.	$33,000;	$30,000;	$18,000;	$9,000.
B.	$33,000;	$30,000;	$20,000;	$7,000.
C.	$36,000;	$30,000;	$18,000;	$6,000.
D.	$36,000;	$30,000;	$18,000;	$8,000.

PROBLEM #18

Haley of Savage bought a shorts and top outfit at Funk's Fine Fashions in
Prior Lake. Funks was having a 25% off spring sale plus another 15% off the
sale price on any shorts and top outfit. If the original price of the outfit was
$80.00, how much did Haley save? How much did Haley pay for the outfit?
A. $29 saved; $51 paid.   B. $32 saved; $48 paid.
C. $20 saved; $60 paid.   D. $12 saved; $68 paid.

LESSON #72   MONEY
WARMUPS
1. $14.25 − $5   4. $65.75   6. 7½ ÷ 1¼   9. 4^3
2. $14.25 − $.50   × .08   7. 9 − 2 3\8   10. $\sqrt{16/64}$
3. $.28 ÷ 14   5. ⅔ of $48?   8. $20 − $5.57

SOLVE THE FOLLOWING:
11. 7T − 13 = 29   12. 8I = 5I + 18   13. 9 / M = 15 / 10

PROBLEM #14
Which is the best buy?
  A. 10 used books for $34.50?   B. 8 used books for $26.50?
  C. Used books at $3.50 each?   D. 5 used books for $17.00?

PROBLEM #15
Bud of McAllen sells chemicals to big oil refining companies. During his swing through southeast Texas last week, Bud sold $48,000 in chemicals. Bud gets 8% commission on his first $20,000 in sales each week and 12% on all sales over $20,000. How much commission did Bud make on his southeast Texas swing last week?
  A. $ 3,840.00   B. $ 5,760.00   C. $ 4,960.00   D. $ 3,760.00

PROBLEM #16
Gail of Mezgerville bought a "Jumbo Crayfish & Oyster Pizza" at Skip's Super Seafood Pizzas in Seabrook. Skip's "Jumbo Crayfish & Oyster Pizza" usually sells for $24.50. However, Gail got the senior citizen's discount of 15%. How much did Gail save on the pizza? How much did Gail pay for the pizza?
  A. $ 3.68 saved; $ 20.82 paid.   B. $ 2.42 saved; $ 21.78 paid.
  C. $ 4.84 saved; $ 19.36 paid.   D. $ 6.05 saved; $ 18.15 paid.

PROBLEM #17
The Junior Class at R.A. Long High School made $960.00 on their Cinco De Mayo Car Wash. They split the money this way: Jr. Prom decorations 1/3, Junior Tea 1/6, Junior Day refreshments 1/5, the rest they put away for their graduation party next year. How much money from the Junior Car Wash went to: the Jr. Prom? the Junior Tea? Junior Day refreshments? the Graduation party?

	Prom	Tea	Refreshments	Graduation Party
A.	$360;	$180;	$228;	$192
B.	$320;	$160;	$192;	$288
C.	$320;	$160;	$208;	$272
D.	$360;	$180;	$192;	$228

PROBLEM #18
Sandy's Pottery and Glass store in Del Rio sells official Rio Grande Valley pottery coffee cups to tourists. Doug of Dickinson bought some to take back to his North Dakota relatives. He bought two 6oz. cups at $3.25 each, four 8oz. cups at $4.25 each, and five 10oz. cups at $4.75 each. How much did Doug spend? How much change did Doug get back from a $50 bill?
A. $ 49.25; $ .75   B. $ 47.25; $ 2.75
C. $ 42.50; $ 7.50   D. $ 52.25; None - Doug had to pay $2.25 more.

WARMUPS

1. 21.3 – 4
2. 21.3 – 40
3. 21.3 – .4

4. $20 – $13.37
5. 40% of $60.55
6. 2/5 of $60.55

7. 8 1/5
    – 7 2/3
8. $15 ÷ .005

9. $(2/5)^3$
10. $\sqrt{225}$

SOLVE THE FOLLOWING:

11. $40/ T = 80 / 100   **12.** 9 / 12 = I / $44   **13.** 10M – $48 = $12.50

USE THE FOLLOWING INFORMATION FOR QUESTIONS 14-18.

Bagger Gable from Bridgeport was making tacos for his Texarkana relatives. He bought the following items: 36 tortillas, 8 lbs of ground beef, 4 tomatoes, 2 onions, 1 lb of grated american cheese, 3 heads of lettuce, 2 bottles of taco sauce, and 4 cans of refried beans. He bought these at Denise's 24 Hour Market in Denton. The prices of the items were: a dozen tortillas for $1.70, ground beef - 2 lbs for $4.18, tomatoes- 3 for $1.20, onions - 2 for $.83, american cheese - $3.17 per lb., 2 heads of lettuce for $1.12, taco sauce - $1.21 per bottle, and refried beans - 2 cans for $1.91.

PROBLEM #14

What did the tortillas cost Bagger Gable?
    A. $1.70   B. $5.10   C. $3.40   D. $2.55

PROBLEM #15

How much did Bagger pay for the ground beef? The tomatoes?
A. $9.36; $1.60 tomatoes.   B. $16.72; $2.40 tomatoes.
C. $16.72; $1.60 tomatoes.   D. $9.36; $2.40 tomatoes.

PROBLEM #16

What did the onions and lettuce cost Bagger Gable?
    A. $1.66 onions; $1.12 lettuce.   B. $1.66 onions; $1.68 lettuce.
    C. $ .83 onions; $1.12 lettuce.   D. $ .83 onions; $1.68 lettuce.

PROBLEM #17

What did Bagger pay for the cheese and beans?
    A. $3.17 cheese: $3.82 beans.   B. $3.17 cheese: $7.64 beans.
    C. $6.34 cheese: $3.82 beans.   D. $6.34 cheese: $7.64 beans.

PROBLEM #18

What was Bagger Gable's total grocery bill at Denise's Market? How much change did he get from a $50 bill?
    A. $26.98 bill; $23.02 change.   B. $32.92 bill; $17.08 change.
    C. $29.38 bill; $20.62 change.   D. None of these.

LESSON #74   MONEY

WARMUPS
1. $36.36 – $4   4. $36.40   6. 7 1/2 × 4/5   8.   .2 ÷ 50
2. $36.36 – $40   × .4   7. 4⅓   9.   3⁴
3. $36.36 + $4.64   5. 2/5 × 45   −1¾   10. √625

SOLVE THE FOLLOWING PROPORTIONS:
11. 12 / 15 = N / 35   **12.** 9 / N = 60 / 100   **13.** 14 = 40% of ?

USE THE FOLLOWING INFORMATION FOR PROBLEMS 14-18.

Randy's Market Place in Pt. Loma has a sale on gallons of natural apple juice. The regular price of the apple juice to the public is $7.50 a gallon. Randy buys the gallons for $3.50 each. Natural apple juice comes in cases of four one gallon jugs to the case. Randy gets a $3.00 rebate on each case he buys.

PROBLEM #14
After the $3.00 a case rebate, what is Randy's cost for a gallon of natural apple juice?
    A. $3.50   B. $3.00   C. $2.75   D. $2.50

PROBLEM #15
How much profit does Randy make on a case of natural apple juice?
    A. $14.00   B. $11.00   C. $17.50   D. $ 19.00

PROBLEM #16
If Randy sells the apple juice for $7.50 a gallon, what percent of the selling price is Randy's profit?
    A. 50%   B. 63.3%   C. 33.3%   D. 36.7%

PROBLEM #17
If Randy puts the gallons of apple juice on sale for $4.00 a gallon, how much profit will he make on each gallon?
    A. $ .50   B. $ 1.25   C. $ 1.50   D. $ 1.00

PROBLEM #18
What percent of the $4.00 sale price of the gallons of apple juice is Randy's profit for a gallon of juice?
    A. 33⅓%   B. 31.25%   C. 30.5%   D. 68.75%

WARMUPS

1. 44.4 – 5   4. 5 1/2 × 6/11   7. .006 ÷ 50   9. $(3/5)^3$
2. 44.4 – 50   5. 24 ÷ 2/3   8. $51.15   10. $\sqrt{.0016}$
3. 44.4 – .5   6. 24 – 9 5/7   × .08

SOLVE THE FOLLOWING:

11. 8T = 5T – 42   **12.** 48 / 9 = I / 6   **13.** What are the area and perimeter of a square with 11 cm sides?

The Trinkles of Gardena had a big three day garage sale. Friday they had sales of $755.75. Saturday was big with sales of $1,847.55, but Sunday the sales fell off again to $727.30. The Trinkle family split the money this way: Ric & Terri 1/3, Tim & Kathy 1/5, Tony & Judy 1/4, and Dale & Edyth the rest.

PROBLEM #14

What was Ric & Terri's share of the garage sale?
A. $1,110.20   B. $666.12   C. $591.15   D. $1,010.60

PROBLEM #15

What was Tony & Judy's share of the money?
A. $666.12   B. $721.63   C. $954.20   D. $832.65

PROBLEM #16

What was Dale & Edyth's share?
A. $591.15   B. $721.63   C. $666.12   D. $744.12

PROBLEM #17

How much more than Tim & Kathy did Tony & Judy get?
A. $55.51   B. $444.08   C. $166.53   D. $277.47

PROBLEM #18

How much more than Ric & Terri did Tony & Judy get?
A. $111.02   B. $444.08   C. $55.51   D. Actually Ric & Terri got $277.55 more than Tony & Judy.

(75)

LESSON #76   GRAPH (Bar)
Warm Ups
1. 36.2 – 5   4. 28 ÷ .004   6. 3/4 × $36   9. 6^3
2. 36.2 – .5   5. $75.75   7. 6 – 2 7/8   10. $\sqrt{169}$
3. 36.2 – 50   ×   .09   8. 7/8 ÷ 1 3/4
SOLVE THE FOLLOWING PROPORTIONS AND EQUATIONS
11. 45/27 = T/24   **12.** 24 = 75% of ?   **13.** 4T – 13 = 27

USE THE FOLLOWING GRAPH TO ANSWER QUESTIONS 14-17.

Monthly Sales For Estes College
Football Memorabilia

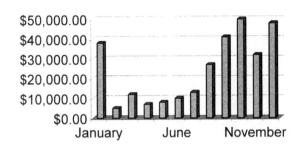

PROBLEM # 14
About how much are the yearly sales at the Estes College Football Memorabilia
Store on Market Street in Houston?
 A. $340,000   B. $280,000   C. $210,000   D. $410,000
PROBLEM # 15
What is a good estimate of the average monthly sales at the Estes College Football
Memorabilia Store?
 A. $15,000   B. $23,000   C. $30,000   D. $35,000
PROBLEM #16
Estimate the average monthly sales during the three best months.
 A. $43,000   B. $25,000   C. $51,000   D. $38,000
PROBLEM #17
What is a good estimate of the average monthly sales during the worst three
months at the Estes College Football Memorabilia Store?
 A. $15,000   B. $12,000   C. $7,000   D. $2,000
PROBLEM #18
Rick, the best salesperson at The Estes Store, sold $6,900 in August, $21,250 in
September, $27,725 in October, $17,150 in November, and $26,795 in December.
If Estes pays 20% commissions on sales, estimate the money Rick made on
commissions during the five month long Texas football season.
 A. $10,000   B. $20,000   C. $30,000   D. $35,000

(76)

LESSON #77   **GRAPH   (Bar)**
WARM UPS
1. $42.78 - 5$ 4. $-8 + -5 - (-4)$ 7. $24\frac{1}{2}$ 9. 10^4
2. $42.78 - 50$ 5. $1\,3/4 \times 5/8$ $-\,9\frac{3}{4}$ 10. $\sqrt{10,000}$
3. $-8 \times -5 \div -4$ 6. 40% of $60.75?   8. $80 \div .005$
SOLVE THE FOLLOWING
11. $25 / 45 = 15 / T$ **12. $I / 60 = 7 / 12$**   **13.** $24 / M = 40 / 100$

NUMBER OF CRUISES IN THE CARIBBEAN

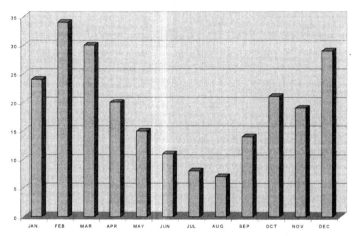

PROBLEM #14
    What is the average number of Caribbean cruises taken per month in the winter
months of December, January, and February?
A. 25   B. 28   C. 31   D. 33
PROBLEM #15
    What is the average number of Caribbean cruises taken per month in the
summer months of June, July, and August?
A. 12   B. 10   C. 8   D. 5
PROBLEM #16
    What is the average number of Caribbean cruises taken in the spring
months of March, April, and May? What is the average for the fall
months of September, October, and November?
A. 21 in spring, 20 in fall.   B. 21 in spring, 19 in fall .
C. 24 in spring, 19 in fall.   D. 24 in spring, 21 in fall.
PROBLEM #17
    What percent of the total Caribbean cruises taken yearly happen
in the four month period of December thru March?
A. 40%   B. 45%   C. 50%   D. 55%
PROBLEM #18
    What percent of the total Caribbean cruises happen in February?
What percent happen in August?
A. 13%,   2%.   B. 15%,   3%.   C. 17%,   2%.   D. 11%,   3%.

(77)

LESSON #78   GRAPH (Line)

WARMUPS
1. 34.62 – 6
2. 34.62 – .6
3. 34.62 – 60

4. -4 + -13 –(-17)
5. -2 × -50 ÷ -4
6. ¾ × $48

7. 24 ÷ . 0008
8. $48.00
   × _____.75

9. $(3/5)^2$
10. $\sqrt{16/36}$

SOLVE THE FOLLOWING:
11. 60 / W = 75 / 100   12. S + 18 = 15   13. 7U + 5U = 2U + 30

Weight Gain

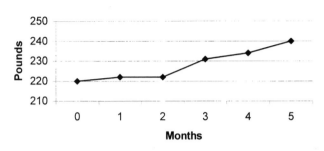

Months

Scott Selby is a receiver for the Washington State Cougars. He was weighed
at 220 pounds when he entered the University. His coach wanted him to be
at least 235 pounds before the next season.

PROBLEM #14
At what month had Scott first reached the coach's goal?
A. Month 1   B. Month 2   C. Month 3   D. Month 5

PROBLEM #15
Between which two months did Scott's weight stay the same?
Months: A 0 to 1   B. 1 to 2   C. 2 to 3   D. 3 to 4

PROBOLEM #16
How many total pounds did Scott gain during the 5 months?
A. 240 lbs.   B. 20 lbs   C. 15 lbs.   D. 245 lbs.

PROBLEM #17
What was Scott's final weight after the 5 months?
A. 220 lbs   B. 230 lbs.   C. 240 lbs   D. 245 lbs

PROBLEM #18
Between which two months was Scott's weight gain the greatest?
A. 0 to 1   B. 2 to 3   C. 3 to 4   D. 4 to 5

(**78**)

LESSON #79 **GRAPH** (Line)
WARMUPS
1. $36.4 - 5$ 4. $\frac{1}{2} \times \$78$ 7. $\$78.00$ 9. 5^4
2. $36.4 - 50$ 5. $\frac{3}{4} \div \frac{2}{3}$ $\underline{\times \quad .05}$ 10. $\sqrt{81}$
3. $36.4 - .5$ 6. $.008 \div 40$ 8. $40 \div .008$
SOLVE THE FOLLOWING:
11. $24 / 40 = 72 / T$ 12. $T / 60 = 20 / 100$ 13. $8T - T = 56$

Dallas Mavericks Wins

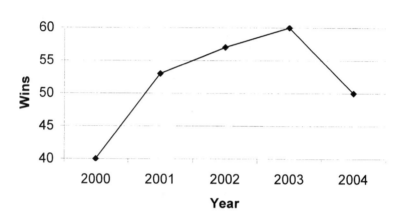

PROBLEM # 14
How many games did the Dallas Mavericks win in 2003 season?
A. 40 B. 53 C. 50 D. 60

PROBLEM #15
How many more games did the Mavericks win in 2004 than in 2000?
A. 10 B. 20 C. 30 D. 50

PROBLEM #16
How many total games did the Mavericks win in the 2000 and 2003 seasons?
A. 20 B. 40 C. 60 D. 100

PROBLEM #17
Between what two years did the Mavericks improve the most?
A. 2000-2001 B. 2001-2002 C. 2002-2003 D. 2003-2004

PROOBLEM #18
Between what two years did the Mavericks show the least improvement?
A. 2000-2001 B. 2001-2002 C. 2002-2003 D. 2003-2004

(79)

LESSON #80   GRAPH (Circle)
WARMUPS
1. $25 – $7.80   4. ½ × $60,000   7. .002 ÷ 50   9. ($2.00)^7
2. $25 – $.78   5. ⅔ × $60,000   8. 50 ÷ .002   10. $\sqrt{144}$
3. $25 – $78   6. ¾ × $60,000
SOLVE THE FOLLOWING:
11. T + $25 = $20.34   **12.** 7I + I = 2I + $30   **13.** M / $40,000 = 25 / 100

St Rose Fund Raising

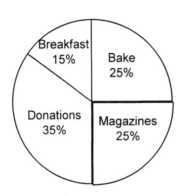

St. Rose School raised $50,000 this year from donations, magazine sales, bake sales and pancake breakfasts.

PROBLEM #14
   Which of the different types of fund raisers was most successful?
   A. Bake sales   B. Magazine sales   C. Pancake breakfasts   D. Donations

PROBLEM #15
   Which two fund raisers brought in the same amount of money?
   A. Pancake breakfasts & Donations   B. Bake sales & Magazine sales
   C. Magazine sales & Donations   D. Bake sales and Pancake breakfasts

PROBLEM #16
   How much money did St. Rose School make on donations?
   A. $12,500   B. $15,000   C. $17,500   D. $20,000

PROBLEM #17
   How much did St Rose School make on bake sales and pancake breakfasts together?
   A. $12,500   B. $15,000   C. $17,500   D. $20,000

PROBLEM #18
   Which fund raiser raised $7,500?
   A. Bake sales   B. Magazine sales   C. Pancake breakfasts   D. Donations

(80)

LESSON #81   **GRAPH**   (Circle)

WARMUPS
1. 51.1 − 7   4. 25 ÷ .002   7. $60.45   9. $(.2)^5$
2. 51.1 − 70   5. .002 ÷ 25   ×   .6   10. $\sqrt{.09}$
3. 51.1 − .7   6. 3 1/2 ÷ 7/8   8. 25% of 500?

SOLVE THE FOLLOWING:
11. 24 / D = 60 / 35   **12.** I / 500 = 15 / 100   **13.** 6M − 17 = 13

Favorite Sport Team

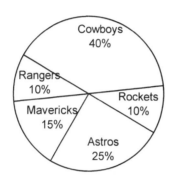

500 students in Texas were surveyed as to what their favorite sport team was from the Dallas Cowboys, Houston Rockets, Texas Rangers, Dallas Mavericks, and the Houston Astros. The percentages chosen are on the graph.

PROBLEM #14
Which team was the most popular?
A. Rockets   B. Cowboys   C. Mavericks   D. Rangers
PROBLEM #15
Which two teams added together were as popular as the Cowboys?
A. Rockets and Astros   B. Mavericks and Rangers
C. Astros and Mavericks   D. Astros and Rangers
PROBLEM #16
The Mavericks and Rangers added together were the same as which team(s)?
A. Rockets   B. Cowboys   C. Astros   D. Rockets and Cowboys
PROBLEM #17
How many of the 500 students chose the Astros?
A. 25   B. 125   C. 250   D. 475
PROBLEM #18
How many students chose the Rangers and the Cowboys?
A. 5 and 20   B. 10 and 40   C. 50 and 200   D. 100 and 400

WARMUPS

1. $45.37 + 6$ 4. $45.37 - 6.6$ 6. $.8 \div 400$ 9. 7^3
2. $45.37 + .6$ 5. $\quad 5\frac{1}{3}$ 7. $400 \div .8$ 10. $\sqrt{36}$
3. $45.37 - 60$ $\underline{-\ 3\frac{1}{4}}$ 8. $7\frac{1}{2} \times 1\frac{1}{3}$

SOLVE THE FOLLOWING:

11. What is the perimeter and area of a rectangle with sides of 8ft. and 6ft.?
12. $9T + T = 60$
13. $4 / T = 12 / 18$

SOLVE THE FOLLOWING:

A standard deck of playing cards has 52 cards, 13 cards in each of four suits {spades (black), hearts (red), diamonds (red), clubs (black)} and four of each kind of card. What is the probability of drawing:

PROBLEM #14
A king that is red?
A. 1/13   B. 2/13   C. 1/4   D. 1/26

PROBLEM #15
A red card and then a black card after putting the red card back in the deck.? (This is called replacement).
A. 1/2   B. 1   C. 2/13   D. 1/4

PROBLEM #16
Two aces without replacing the first ace?
A. 1/13   B. 1/26   C. 1/221   D. 1/2,652

PROBLEM #17
Five cards in the spades suit without replacing the cards?
A. 1/625   B. 51/102,685   C. 33/66,640   D. 1/1024

PROBLEM #18
Four kings without replacement?
A. 4/86,632   B. 1/270,725   C. 1/21,658   D. 1/1,616

LESSON #83   PROBABILITY

WARMUPS
1. 15.1 − 2   4. $25 − $13.64   7. 36 ÷ .0009   9. $(.2)^3$
2. 15.1 − 20   5. 3/4 × $60   8. 25% of $60?   10. $\sqrt{400}$
3. 15.1 − .2   6. 8 2/5 ÷ 7

SOLVE THE FOLLOWING:
11. 24 / 20 = **M** / 30
12. 8 / 5 = 20 / **M**
13. 11M + 2M = 7M + 15

PROBLEM #14
Ed and Lindy had two children. What is the probability that they had one boy and one girl?
   A. 1/   B. 1/2   C. 3/4 D. 1/8

PROBLEM #15
When Ed and Lindy had a third child, what was the probability that they were all boys?
   A. 1/4 B. 1/2   C. 3/4   D. 1/8

PROBLEM #16
What was the probability that at least two out of the three children were girls?
   A. 1/4   B. 1/2   C. 3/4   D. 1/8

PROBLEM #17
If the first child out of the three was a boy, what is the probability that they would have exactly two boys?
   A. 1/4   B. 1/2   C. 3/4   D. 1/8

PROBLEM #18
Ed and Lindy already had three girls. When their fourth child was born, what was the probability of it being a girl?
   A. 1/4   B. 1/2   C. 1/16   D. 1/8

(83)

LESSON #84   PROBABILITY

WARMUPS
1. 25.7 − 30
2. 25.7 − .003
3. -7 + -6 +10
4. -7 − (-6) + -10
5. -3 × -10 ÷ 2
6.   15
    − 7 ⅔
7. 18 ÷ ⅔
8. .4 ÷ 80
9. (-3)³
10. √289

SOLVE THE FOLLOWING:
11. Find the area and circumference of a circle with a radius of ten inches. Use 3.14 for pi.
12. 40 / 25 = 32 / **T**
13. 8T − T = -56

SOLVE THE FOLLOWING PROBABILITY PROBLEMS:
Kamber has six pairs of gloves. They are the same except for colors. She has three pairs of black, two pairs of gray and one pair of white. She put them all in a sack and drew them out without looking at what she was drawing out.

PROBLEM #14
What is the probability of pulling out a white glove first?
A. 1/12   B. 1/6   C. 1/3   D. 1/2

PROBLEM #15
What is the probability of drawing out a left handed glove?
A. 1/12   B. 1/6   C. 1/3   D. 1/2

PROBLEM #16
What is the probability of drawing out two black gloves in two draws?
A. 5/24   B. 5/22   C. 1/4   D. 1/2

PROBLEM #17
What is the least amount of draws Kamber would have to make to get at least one left glove and one right glove?
A. 2   B. 3   C. 7   D. 12

PROBLEM #18
What is the least amount of draws she would have to make to be sure she got a left and a right gray glove?
A. 6   B. 12   C. 11   D. 7

LESSON #85   PROBABILITY

WARMUPS

1. 32.2 – 6
2. 32.2 – 60
3. 32.2 – .6
4. 3/4 of $40?
5. 2/5 of $40?
6. 75% of $40?
7. 7/8 ÷ 1 2/5
8. 20 – 4 6/7
9. $(1/5)^3$
10. $\sqrt{121}$

SOLVE THE FOLLOWING:

11. 14 / T = 35 / 40
12. 18 / ½ = **I** / 4
13. What is the perimeter and area of a right triangle with legs equal to 5" and 12", and a hypotenuse of 13"?

PROBLEM #14

A standard die has six sides with the numbers one through six shown on the sides. What are the odds of rolling a 3 or a 4?

A. 1/6   B. 1/3   C. 1/2   D. 2/5

PROBLEM #15

If a standard die is rolled twice, what are the odds of rolling a three and then a four?

A. 1/6   B. 1/3   C. 1/36   D. 7/12

PROBLEM #16

When two dice are rolled together there are possible values from two through twelve. What are the odds of rolling a three?

A. 1/18   B. 1/12   C. 1/4   D. 1/36

PROBLEM #17

When two dice are rolled together, what are the odds of rolling a six?

A. 1/9   B. 5/36   C. 7/36   D. 1/6

PROBLEM #18

When two dice are rolled together, what are the odds of rolling an even number?

A. 1/2   B. 5/12   C. 5/9   D. 6/11

(85)

LESSON #86   PROBABILITY

WARMUPS
1. 23.36 – 8
2. 23.36 – .8
3. 23.36 – 80
4. 3/4 of $60?
5. 5/6 of $60?
6. 3/5 of $60?
7. 38 1/2 + 11 3/4
8. 24 ÷ .006
9. $(3/5)^3$
10. $\sqrt{.0016}$

SOLVE THE FOLLOWING:
11. 24 = ?% of 60? 12. 10 / 25 = K / 100 13. What is the area and perimeter of a 8" by 10" rectangle?

A standard deck of card has 52 cards divided into four suits: red (hearts and diamonds), black (spades and clubs). Also there are four kings, four queens, four jacks, etc.

PROBLEM #14
Monte was a betting fool. He once wanted to bet that he could draw a black king from a standard deck of cards. What were the odds of him doing that?
    A. 1/52   B. 1/13   C. 1/26   D. 1/2

PROBLEM #15
Elaine was much more conservative. She wanted to bet that she could roll an even number on a six sided die. What were the chances of her doing that?
    A. 1/2   B. 1/6   C. 1/3   D. 1

PROBLEM #16
What is the probability that both Monte and Elaine won their bets?
    A. 1/78   B. 1/52   C. 1/26   D. 7/13

PROBLEM #17
What are the odds of Ralph and Suzie having exactly three boys and one girl if they had four children?
    A. 1/16   B. 3/16   C. 1/3   D. 1/4

PROBLEM #18
Pedro had four shirts with Baylor logos on them. Two were white, one was blue and one was tan. He had three pairs of bermuda shorts. One was tan, one was black and the other was yellow. One day the Waco power station got hit by lightening and Pedro had to dress in the dark. He just grabbed a shirt and a pair of shorts at random. What was the probability he was dressed in all tan?
    A. 3/16   B. 1/6   C. 1/12   D. 7/12

LESSON #87   EQUATIONS

WARMUPS

1. $34.7 - 6$
2. $34.7 - 60$
3. $34.7 - .6$
4. $34.7 + 6 + 3.47$
5. $2.4 \div .08$
6. $.24 \div -8$
7. $3/4 \div 2\ 1/4$
8. $7 - 4\ 2/5$
9. $(-2)^3$
10. $\sqrt{169}$

SOLVE THE FOLLOWING

11. $7U - 33 = 23$
12. $6C + 55 = C-15$
13. $24 / L = 36 / 42$

PROBLEM # 14
If four times a number is decreased by three, the result is 21. Find the number.
   A. 4½   B. 6   C. 14   D. 20

PROBLEM #15
If five times a number is increased by five, the result is 55. Find the number.
   A. 5   B. 8   C. 10   D. 12

PROBLEM #16
If a number is decreased by 12, the result is 30. Find the number.
   A. 8   B. 18   C. 42   D. 360

PROBLEM #17
Eight plus three times a number is equal to 23. Find the number.
   A. 5   B. 7⅔   C. 10⅓   D. 45

PROBLEM #18
Twenty-eight is equal to three times a number decreased by 11. Find the number.
   A. 5⅔   B. 6   C. 9   D. 13

WARMUPS

1. $28.2 \times .4$
2. $28.2 \div .004$
3. $28.2 - 4$
4. $28.2 - 40$
5. $9 - 6\ 5/9$
6. $7\ 1/2 \times 3/5$
7. $10\frac{1}{2} \div 7$
8. 40% of \$35 =?
9. $(-3)^4$
10. $\sqrt{9/36}$

SOLVE THE FOLLOWING

11. $5B + 22 = 2B + 49$
12. $15 / 12 = R / 8$
13. Find the perimeter and area of a rectangle that is 8ft. by 12ft.

PROBLEM #14
Four times a number increased by four is the same as two times the number. Find the number.
  A. -4   B. -2   C. 2   D. 4

PROBLEM #15
Eight times a number decreased by two times that number is equal to 30. Find the number.
  A. 3   B. 3½   C. 5   D. 12

PROBLEM #16
Three increased by five times a number is the same as three times that number. Find the number.
  A. -1½   B. -⅔   C. 0   D. ⅔

PROBLEM #17
Find a number such that six times the number is the same as eight decreased by two times that number.
  A. -1   B. 0   C. 1   D. 2

PROBLEM #18
Twelve increased by three times a number is the same as nine times the number. Find the number.
  A. -1   B. 1   C. 2   D. 3

(88)

WARMUPS

1. $3.6 \div 8$
2. $.36 \div 8$
3. $36 \div .008$
4. $12.4 - 7$
5. $12.4 - 70$
6. $7/8 \times 1\ 3/5$
7. $21 - 7\frac{1}{3}$
8. $21\frac{1}{3} - 7\frac{3}{4}$
9. 7^3
10. $\sqrt{121}$

SOLVE THE FOLLOWING:
11. $80 / T = 32 / 6$ **12.** $36 = 75\%$ of ?   **13.** $8M + 2 = 5M + 8$

PROBLEM #14
   Eight more than five times a number equals two more than eight times the same number. Find the number.
   A. 2/5   B. 1 1/2   C. 2   D. 4

PROBLEM #15
   Find a number such that four less than six times the number equals three times the number increased by twelve.
   A. 2   B. 4½   C. 5   D. 5⅓

PROBLEM #16
   If fifteen times a number increased by two is the same as ten times the number increased by four, find the number.
   A. 2/5   B. 14/17   C. 1   D. 1 1/2

PROBLEM #17
   Three times a number decreased by that number itself is the same as four times that number decreased by ten. Find the number.
   A. 0   B. 3   C. 5   D. 10

PROBLEM #18
   One half some number decreased by four is equal to -6.
Find the number.
   A. -20   B. -4   C. -2   D. 4

LESSON #90   EQUATIONS

WARMUPS

1. $41.6 - 5$
2. $41.6 - .5$
3. $41.6 - 50$
4. $\frac{3}{4} \times \$48$
5. 75% of $48?
6. $9 - 4\frac{1}{4}$
7. $5\frac{1}{3} \div 2\frac{2}{3}$
8. $-8 + -5 - (-6)$
9. $(-5)^3$
10. $\sqrt{625}$

SOLVE THE FOLLOWING:

11. $8(M+3) = 72$ **12.** $9M - 6M = M + -18$
13. $8 / K = 20 / 30$

PROBLEM #14
   Three times the sum of a number and four is 18. Find
the number.
   A. 2   B. $4\frac{2}{3}$ C. 10   D. 27

PROBLEM #15
   Seven times the difference between a number and two equals
fourteen. Find the number.
   A. 0   B. 2 2/7   C. 2 4/5   D. 4

PROBLEM #16
   If three times the sum of two times a number and four is 24, find
the number.
   A. -2   B. 2   C. $3\frac{1}{3}$ D. $4\frac{2}{3}$

PROBLEM #17
   Two times the sum of a number and three is equal to four times
the sum of that number and four. Find the number.
   A. -5   B. $-\frac{1}{2}$ C. $\frac{1}{2}$ D. 5

PROBLEM #18
   Find a number such that fifteen times the number decreased by
twenty times the number is -45.
   A. -9   B. -5   C. $1\frac{2}{3}$ D. 9

(90)

LESSON #91   EQUATIONS

WARMUPS

1. 37.2 – 8
2. 37.2 – 80
3. -5 + -6 – (-11)
4. -100 ÷ -5 ÷ 2
5. 60% of $75?
6. 3/5 of $75
7. 4½ ÷ 3
8. 6⅓ – 4¾
9. 10^5
10. $\sqrt{400}$

SOLVE THE FOLLOWING:
11. 5T+ 6T = -3T + 42
12. 3M + 5(M+1) = 61
13. 14 / 21 = 8 / **R**

PROBLEM #14
Find two consecutive integers whose sum is 35.
A. 5 and 7   B. -5 and -7   C. 17 and 18   D. -17 and -18

PROBLEM #15
Find three consecutive integers whose sum is 36.
A. 10, 12, 14   B. 11, 12, 13   C. 2, 3, 6   D. -10, -12, -14

PROBLEM #16
Find three consecutive even integers whose sum is 48.
A. 14, 16, 18   B. 15, 16, 17   C. 2, 4, 6   d. -2, -4, -6

PROBLEM #17
Find three consecutive odd integers whose sum is -3.
A. -2, -1, 0   B. -3, -1, 1   C. -3, 0, -3   D. 0, 3, 6

PROBLEM #18
Find three consecutive integers such that the sum of the first and third is twenty-four.
A. 6, 8, 10   B. 10, 12, 14   C. 11, 12, 13   D. 8, 12, 16

Think "how much time and money a classroom set of
Practice Practice Practice will save!!!"

LESSON #92   EQUATIONS

WARMUPS

1. $-8 \times 5 \div -2$
2. $-8 - -5 + -2$
3. $71.1 - 90$
4. $71.1 - 9$
5. $71.1 - .9$
6. $\$20 - \$3.57$
7. $\frac{2}{3} \times \$24$
8. $12 - 7\frac{1}{4}$
9. $(1/2)^4$
10. $\sqrt{\frac{1}{4}}$

SOLVE THE FOLLOWING:

11. What is the perimeter and area of a right triangle with sides of 15 inches and 20 inches and a hypotenuse of 25 inches?
12. $9U + 3U = 5U + 84$
13. $3M + 5(M+2) = 4(M+1) + -14$

PROBLEM #14

Find three consecutive even integers such that four times the first integer is equal to three times the third integer.
    A. 2, 4, 6   B. 6, 7, 8   C. 6, 8, 10   D. 12, 14, 16

PROBLEM #15

Find four consecutive integers such that the sum of the first and fourth is twenty-five.
    A. 11, 12, 13, 14   B. 5, 10, 15, 20
    C. 14, 15, 16, 17   D. -5, 10, 20, 30

PROBLEM #16

Find three consecutive integers such that the sum of the first two is twenty-one more than the third.
    A. 10, 11, 12   B. 13, 15, 17   C. 17, 18, 19   D. 22, 23, 24

PROBLEM #17

The sum of three consecutive even integers is the same as two more than two times the 2nd integer. Find the integers.
    A. -2, 0, 2   B. 0, 2, 4   C. 2, 4, 6   D. 4, 6, 8

PROBLEM #18

Find four consecutive integers such that twice the second integer is equal to the sum of the first, third, and fourth integers.
    A. -3, -2, -1, 0   B. 0, 1, 2, 3
    C. 4, 5, 6, 7   D. 10, 11, 12, 13

LESSON #93   EQUATIONS

WARMUPS

1. 31.3 – 5   4. $20 + $23 + $4.77   6. 8 ½   8. $25.76 – $19
2. 31.3 – .5   5. ¾ ÷ ⅔   + 6 ⅔   9. 10^3
3. 31.3 – 50   7. .24 ÷ 60   10. $\sqrt{49}$

SOLVE THE FOLLOWING:
11. 30 / 18 = 45 / **B**
12. 25 / .004 = **B** / 8
13. 20B = 17B + 81

PROBLEM #14
The sum of three consecutive multiples of four is 48. What is the sum of the next three higher multiples of four?
  A. 84   B. 60   C. 64   D. 80

PROBLEM #15
Five less than three times a number is the same as seven times the number plus fifteen. What is the number?
  A. -5   B. 5   C. -10   D. 10

PROBLEM #16
Mr. Suek from San Antonio is three years less than four times his son's age. In six years Mr. Suek will be five years less than three times his son's age. How old are Mr. Suek and his son?
  A. Mr. Suek 37   Son 10   B. Mr. Suek 45   Son 12
  C. Mr. Suek 57   Son 15   D. Mr. Suek 69   Son 18

PROBLEM #17
The sum of three consecutive odd integers is ninety-nine. What would the sum of the smallest and the largest number be?
  A. 64   B. 66   C. 68   D. 99

PROBLEM #18
Last basketball season UCLA had ten more wins than Oklahoma and four more wins than Oregon. Texas had three more wins than Oklahoma. Find the number of wins each school had last season if three times UCLA's wins plus Oklahoma's wins equals 102 wins.
  A. UCLA 28   OREGON 24   TEXAS 15   OKLAHOMA 18
  B. UCLA 30   OREGON 26   TEXAS 23   OKLAHOMA 20
  C. UCLA 30   OREGON 26   TEXAS 17   OKLAHOMA 20
  D. UCLA 28   OREGON 24   TEXAS 21   OKLAHOMA 18

(93)

LESSON #94   PROBLEM SOLVING (GUESS & CHECK)

WARMUPS
1. $50.18 - 8$
2. $50.18 - 80$
3. $50.18 - .8$
4. $-5 \times -8 \div -20$
5. $-10 - (-8) + 5$
6. $-5(6 - (-8))$
7. $3\,1/3 \times 15/18$
8. $20\frac{1}{4} - 15\frac{2}{3}$
9. 20^3
10. $\sqrt{400}$

SOLVE THE FOLLOWING
11. $8 / 12 = 20 / M$ **12.** $25 / 45 = M / 100$ 13. What is the area and perimeter of a right triangle with legs of ten and twenty-four inches and a hypotenuse of 26 inches?

PROBLEM #14
Tom & Kathy's ages are 3 years apart. Their ages add up to 101. How old are they?
   A. 50 & 51   B. 50½   C. 49 & 52   D. 48 & 53

PROBLEM #15
Alex had eight more strikeouts than Kevin. Together they had 54 strikeouts. How many strikeouts did Alex have?
   A. 23   B. 27   C. 29   D. 31

PROBLEM #16
Trenton has ten coins made up of nickels, dimes and quarters. If he has $1.05, how many nickels does he have?
   A. 7   B. 1   C. 5   D. 3

PROBLEM #17
Juan is 3 years younger than Miguel. Jose is 5 years older than Miguel. If the sum of their ages is 95, how old is Jose?
   A. 36   B. 31   C. 40   D. 33

PROBLEM #18
Harley is nine years older than Charlie. If you reverse the digits in their ages and then add them together, you get 141. How old is Charlie?
   A. 66   B. 67   C. 74   D. 57

LESSON #95   PROBLEM SOLVING (DRAW A PICTURE)

WARMUPS
1. 52.29 – 7
2. 52.29 –70
3. 52.29 – .7

4. -8 × -10 ÷ 5
5. 10 –(-5) + -15
6. 3 1/3 ÷ 1 1/9

7. $55.56
   ×   .22
8. 22 – 7 3/4

9. $(-5)^4$
10. $\sqrt{9/36}$

SOLVE THE FOLLOWING:
11. 30 / 25 = 9 / T   **12.** 15 = ?% of 25   **13.** 8T = 11T + 42

PROBLEM #14
Two cars were driving on I-90 going opposite directions. One left Moses Lake going east and the other one left Spokane going west. The car traveling from Moses Lake had driven 58 miles. The car from Spokane had driven 63 miles. If Moses Lake is 98 miles west of Spokane, how far apart are the cars?
    A. 40 miles   B. 35 miles   C. 5 miles   D. 23 miles

PROBLEM #15
A motorhome is 35 ft. long. The bedroom is ½ as long as the kitchen/living room and twice as long as the driving area. How long is the bedroom?
    A. 5 ft.   B. 10 ft.   C. 20 ft.   D. 15 ft.

PROBLEM #16
Bud from Amarillo is filling a 20 gallon barrel with water. He's using a 5 gallon bucket. The barrel has a hole in it so that for every 5 gallons he puts in 2 gallons leak out. How many buckets does Bud have to put in to fill the barrel?
    A. 7 buckets   B. 6 buckets   C. 6⅔ buckets   d. 4 buckets

PROBLEM #17
A Hummer driven by Ben and a Mustang convertible driven by Hanna start at the same time twenty miles apart on I-10. Ben starts on the east side of Houston and drives east on I-10 at 65 mph. Hanna starts on the west side of Houston and drives west on I-10 at 70 mph. How far apart are Ben and Hanna after three hours?
    A. 425 mi.   B. 420 mi.   C. 440 mi.   D. 385 mi.

PROBLEM #18
Barbie M. from Longview is going to paint a wall 3 different colors for her Washington State Cougar client, Greg. The colors are crimson at the top, light grey in the middle and dark grey on the bottom. The crimson stripe is ½ as tall as the light grey stripe and the dark grey stripe is 1½ times as tall as the crimson stripe. If the wall is 9 feet tall, how wide is the light grey stripe?
    A. 4 ft.   B. 3 ft.   C. 6 ft.   D. 2 ft.

LESSON #96   PROBLEM SOLVING (TABLE)

WARMUPS
1. 24.2 − 4
2. 24.2 − 40
3. 24.2 − .4
4. -9 + -8 − (-17)
5. 25 × -4 ÷ 10
6. $35 ÷ .007
7. 7½ − 5¾
8. 7 1/3 × 6/11
9. $(¼)^3$
10. $\sqrt{1/25}$

SOLVE THE FOLLOWING:

11. 10T − 25 = 15   **12.** 15 / I = 45 / 12   **13.** What is the area and perimeter of a right triangle with legs of 15 cm and 36 cm whose hypotenuse is 39 cm?

PROBLEM #14
Maria from Pasadena had a job that paid more as she got more experienced. She received $3 a day more each day that she worked. She got paid $15 the first day she worked. How much did she get paid on the fifth day she worked?
    A. $30   B. $15   C. $27   D. $36

PROBLEM #15
How much did Maria get paid for all five days?
    A. $75   B. $135   C. $78   D. $105

PROBLEM #16
Frank from Deer Park also got paid on experience. He received 3 times more each day that he worked. How much did he make on the 5th day if he started at $15 the first day?
    A. $135   B. $1,215   C. $405   D. $225

PROBLEM #17
How much did Frank make in all five days?
    A. $1,815   B. $600   C. $950   D. $2,185

PROBLEM #18
Irene from Spokane worked on a job that paid on experience too. She received the square of the previous days salary. She got $3 the first day. How much did she make on the fifth day?
    A. $6,561   B. $43,046,721   C. $48   D. $21,523,360

(96)

LESSON #97   PROBLEM SOLVING (LOGIC-MIXTURE)
WARMUPS
1. $10.02 - 8.1$ 4. $3\frac{1}{2} \div 14$ 7. $.08 \div 200$ 9. 3^4
2. $10.02 - 81$ 5. $10\frac{1}{5} - 8\frac{2}{3}$ 8. $\begin{array}{r} \$36.06 \\ \times\ .8 \end{array}$ 10. $\sqrt{.09}$
3. $10.02 - .81$ 6. ¾ of \$52?

SOLVE THE FOLLOWING:
11. $15 = 60\%$ of ?   12. $8T = 10T + 18$ 13. $24 / 18 = M / 45$

PROBLEM #14
Juanita, Mario and Tomas enjoyed sports. They all excelled at one sport.
One was a bowler. One was a baseball player and the other one was in
gymnastics. Find out what sport Mario excelled in if; no two of them excelled
at the same sport,   Mario and Juanita played their sports indoors,   Juanita's
sport did not have a ball.
 A. Baseball   B. Bowling   C. Gynmastics D. None

PROBLEM #15
Rachel, Patty, Steve and Mike went to Merrick Middle School in Houston.
Each one had a favorite subject and no two people liked the same subject. The
subjects they liked were: PE , Math, English, Science.
 A girl liked science. A boy liked numbers. Mike loved to write. Rachel hated
sports.   What did Patty like the most?
 A. Math   B. PE   C. Science   D. English

PROBLEM #16
Ken, Tom, and Stan play golf. One plays at Mint Valley G.C., one at
Longview C.C., and the other at 3 Rivers G.C.. Their handicaps are 20, 18 and
11. Each golfer plays a different course.
 The 3 Rivers golfer was better than Stan. The 20 handicapper played at Mint
Valley. The longest name was the middle handicap. Ken is a better golfer than
the Mint Valley Golfer. What course does Ken play at?
 A. 3-Rivers   B. Mint Valley   C. Longview   D. The Woodlands in Houston.

PROBLEM #17
A par in golf is the score a good golfer should get on a hole. (Other golf terms,
Bogie = one over par, Double Bogie = 2 over, Triple Bogie = 3 over, Birdie = 1 under,
Eagle = 2 under). Mr. Taylor, an erratic golfer from lower Skamakoway, was even
par on the Longview Country Club Golf Course on the last four holes. He had no
bogies or double bogies and never had the same type of score twice. Which of the
following four scores would work?
A. Par-Birdie-Birdie-Double Bogie.   B. Birdie-Par-Triple Bogie-Eagle
C. Bogie-Birdie-Bogie-Eagle.   D. Eagle-Par-Triple Bogie- Par

PROBLEM #18
Gene from Everett was 2 under par on the first five holes at the Longview
Country Club. Which of these scores for the first five holes would give Gene two
under par?
A. Birdie-Birdie-Birdie-Double Bogie-Eagle   B. Par-Par-Birdie-Birdie-Bogie
C. Birdie-Double Bogie-Birdie-Par-Eagle   D. Bogie-Par-Double Bogie-Par-Birdie

LESSON #98   PROBLEM SOLVING (VENN DIAGRAMS)

WARMUPS
1. $85.24 - 7$ 4. $-9 + -8 - (-6)$ 7. $71.17   9. $(-2)^3$
2. $85.24 - 70$ 5. $-3 \times 10 \div -2$ $\times$ .08   10. $\sqrt{.0016}$
3. $85.24 - 7.7$ 6. $.002 \div 80$ 8. $3\ 3/4 \times 8/15$

SOLVE THE FOLLOWING:
11. $-7T + 28 = 70$ **12.** $24 / 45 = T / 20$ **13.** $40 = 80\%$ OF ?

PROBLEM #14
One semester, at Clover Park Middle School, 48 students got an "A" in math and 56 students got an "A" in science. If 10 students got an "A" in both, how many only got an "A" in: 1. Math?   2. Science?
   A. 58 math; 66 science.   B. 28 math; 36 sceince.
   C. 38 math; 46 science   D. 10 math; 10 science.

PROBLEM #15
In problem number 14, how many students got an "A" in science or math?
   A. 94   B. 104   C. 10   D. 124

PROBLEM #16
Twenty middle school boys were asked what sports they played. Nine played football, 10 played basketball, and 3 played both. How many didn't play either sport?
   A. 0   B. 2   C. 4   D. 7

PROBLEM #17
Fifteen kids went to a movie. Seven had popcorn, 5 had candy, 6 had a soda, 2 had popcorn and candy, 2 had candy and a soda, 1 had popcorn and a soda. Nobody had all three. How many didn't have anything?
   A. 0   B. 2   C. 4   D. 7

PROBLEM #18
Twenty-five girls were polled about what sports they play. Twelve play volleyball. 11 run track, 16 play basketball, 7 play volleyball & basketball, 8 play basketball and track, 6 play volleyball and track, 5 play all three sports. How many do not play any of these sports?
   A. 0   B. 2   C. 4   D. 7

WARMUPS
1. $20.55 − $7   4. $20.55 ÷ .005   7. 25% of $32.80?   9. $(3/4)^3$
2. $20.55 − $70   5. 3 3/4 × 8/25   8. $20 ÷ 2/3   10. $\sqrt{625}$
3. $20.55 − $.70   6. 12 − 5 5/8

SOLVE THE FOLLOWING:
11. 35 / 40 = T /100   **12.** 28 = 80% of ?   **13.** 4T − 41 = 39

PROBLEM #14
A salmon was swimming upstream. It came upon some rapids that were 30 feet long. The salmon would leap forward 5 feet at a time, but for each leap he would be washed back 3 feet by the current. How many leaps did the salmon take to make it past the rapids?
    A. 6 leaps   B. 15 leaps   C. 14 leaps   D. He never can make it.

PROBLEM #15
A lizard has a head ¼ as long as its body and a tail twice as long as its body. If its tail is 8 inches long, how long is the lizard?
    A. 18 in.   B. 7 in.   C. 12 in.   D. 13 in.

PROBLEM #16
Twenty-eight students from Chula Vista Middle School went to the San Diego Zoo. 5 students saw the snakes and tigers. 14 students saw the snakes. 4 students saw the tigers and monkeys. 8 students saw the snakes and monkeys. 12 saw the monkeys. 11 students saw the tigers. 3 saw the monkeys, tigers and snakes. How many of the students didn't see any of these 3 animals?
    A. 0   B. 1   C. 2   D. 5

PROBLEM #17
Four students; John, Dave, Mary & Susie signed up for four different subjects at Coweeman Middle School. The subjects were advanced math, art, PE, and music. No student signed up for the same class. A boy signed up for advanced math.   Mary and David did not sign up for music. Susie really liked to draw. What did John sign up for?
    A. advanced math   B. music   C. art   D. PE

PROBLEM #18
In the Monticello Chess Club there were 15 members. During the time they met, each player was to play every other member one time. How many total chess matches were there?
    A. 105   B. 210   C. 225   D. 15

LESSON # 100   TEST PREPARATION

WARMUPS
1. 24.17 − 6
2. 24.17 − 60
3. 24.17 − .6
4. $30.40
   × .06
5. 15 ÷ .003
6. 20 ⅓
   − 7 ½
7. ¾ of $36.00
8. 3½ ÷ ¾
9. 5^4
10. $\sqrt{256}$

SOLVE THE FOLLOWING:
11. $4T − 24 = 36$ 12. $5I = 2I + 45$ 13. $10M + 2M = 7M + 75$

PROBLEM #14
Keoki and Kristen baked a pie in Home Economics. Keoki ate one fifth of the pie and Kristen ate 25% of the pie. What percent did they eat?
   A. 25.2%   B. 30%   C. 35%   D. 45%

PROBLEM #15
Tiffany and Gabbi went on a hike to the Ape Caves. It took them 2½ hours on the way to the Caves. Coming back it took them twice as long. How much time did they spend hiking?
   A. 4½ hours.   B. 6½ hours.   C. 7½ hours.   D. 8½ hours.

PROBLEM #16
Scott from Castle Rock wants to average 18 points a game in this years basketball playoffs. He scored 16, 14, and 20 points in the first three basketball playoff games. How many points does he have to score in his final game to get his desired average?
   A. 18 points   B. 20 points   C. 22 points   D. 24 points

PROBLEM #17
On the new television show "If You Only Knew", the questions are worth three times more than the previous question. If the 5th question is worth $4,050.00, how much was the first question valued at?
   A. $50.00   B. $150.00   C. $810.00   D. $1,350.00

PROBLEM #18
Preston from Presido is saving to buy a new stereo system that costs $400.00. He has saved $155.00 so far. Each week he gets a $15.00 allowance and mows lawns for another $20.00. If he uses all this money to save for the system, how many weeks would it take him to get enough money to buy the stereo system?
   A. 5 weeks.   B. 6 weeks.   C. 7 weeks.   D. 12 weeks.

(100)

LESSON #101   TEST PREPARATION

WARMUPS

1. $24.9 + 7$
2. $24.9 - 70$
3. $24.9 + 77.17$

4. $24 \div .006$
5. $\begin{array}{r} \$80.60 \\ \times \ \ .08 \\ \hline \end{array}$

6. $\frac{3}{4} \div \frac{1}{3}$
7. $\begin{array}{r} 9 \\ - 3\frac{3}{4} \\ \hline \end{array}$

8. 80% of $\$80.60$
9. $(\frac{1}{2})^4$
10. $\sqrt{.09}$

SOLVE THE FOLLOWING

11. $3U + 17 = 38$ 12. $9C = C + 57$ 13. $12 / L = 60 / 35$

PROBLEM #14

The Lake Conway Middle School Drama Club is getting boxes of muffins for a fundraiser. Each container holds 15 muffins. Which amount could be boxed without having any muffins left over?

    A. 115   B. 135   C. 145   D. 200

PROBLEM #15

Mary bought a collector doll for $40 and sold it for $50. She later decided to buy it back for $60 and then resold it for $70. How much money did she lose or make on the sales?

    A. Lost $20   B. Made $20   C. Lost $30   D. Made $30

PROBLEM #16

What is the correct total of: $9 \div \frac{1}{3} \times 3^2$?

    A. 243   B. 162   C. 29   D. 9

PROBLEM #17

The length of a model of a boat is 8 inches. The model is made to be 1/56th of the boat's actual size. Which proportion can be used to find the length (L) of the actual boat?

    A. $L / 8 = 1 / 56$ B. $8 / L = 1 / 56$ C. $8 / 56 = L / 1$ D. $8 / 56 = 1 / L$

PROBLEM #18

Teresa from Tucumcari works at a horse stable. She gets paid $25 a day plus $8 an hour for cleaning the stalls. She made $65 yesterday. How many hours did she work?

    A. 3 hours   B. 4 hours   C. 5 hours   D. 6 hours

WARMUPS
1. 46.18 – 8   4. $45.00   6. 23 ½   8.   20% of $45?
2. 46.18 – .8 $\times$ .2   – 7 ¾   9. 5^4
3. 46.18 – 80   5. 2 1/2 × 8/15   7. .06 ÷ 80   10. $\sqrt{81}$

SOLVE THE FOLLOWING
11. 25 / **B** = 75 / 9   **12.** 34 / 51 = 14 / **R**   **13.** 5U – 18 = 22

PROBLEM #14
Which is the correct order from smallest to largest?
   A. 4.3; 4.14; 4.253; 5   B. 5; 4.3; 4.14; 4.253
   C. 4.14; 4.253; 4.3; 5   D. None of the above.

PROBLEM #15
Dan from Del Rio washes his truck two times a week to get the
west Texas dust off. He kept track of how long it took him each
time last month. It took 35 min;   30 min; 50 min; 25 min; 40 min;
60 min; 30 min; 10 min.
   Based on these times, what is the "MODE" for these times?
   A. 30 min.   B. 32½ min.   C. 35 min.   D. 280 min.

PROBLEM #16
Tim from Temple has a motor scooter that gets 43.2 miles per gallon
of gas. How far can Tim drive if he uses eight gallons of gas?
   A. 5.4 miles.   B. 51.2 miles.   C. 320 miles.   D. 345.6 miles.

PROBLEM #17
Shannon can run the 400 meter race in 58.71 seconds. Her
friend Kristen runs the same race in 59.2 seconds. How much
faster was Shannon's time?
A. 0.49 seconds.   B. 0.51 seconds. C. 1.49 seconds. D. 1.51 seconds.

PROBLEM #18
The lowest temperature in Missoula, Montana on January 18th was
-6 degrees F.. As the day progressed the temperature rose twenty-seven
degrees F. What was the temperature then?
   A. 21 degrees F.   B. 27 degrees F.
   C. 33 degrees F.   D. -33 degrees F.

WARMUPS
1. 36.89 + 7
2. 36.89 – 70
3. 36.89 – 7.7

4. $75.60
   × .003
5. ⅔ × $24

6. 1½ ÷ ¾
7. 8
   –5 ¼

8. 50 ÷ .004
9. 10^5
10. $\sqrt{169}$

SOLVE THE FOLLOWING:
11. 12K + 30 = 90   12. 7A = A + 30   13. 60 / 24 = T / 2

PROBLEM #14
The $\sqrt{67.3}$ is between which pair of consecutive integers?
   A. 33 and 34.   B. 8 and 9.   C. 7 and 8.   D. 6 and 7.

PROBLEM #15
Four teams, of five teachers each, at New Braunfels Middle School
had a weight loss contest from New Years Day till St. Patrick's Day.
Which list shows the four teams weight losses in order from the least
to the most?
   A. 88.1 kg;   87.98 kg;   88.05 kg;   87.435 kg.
   B. 87.96 kg;   88.1 kg;   88.05 kg;   87.435 kg.
   C. 87.96 kg;   87.435 kg;   88.1 kg;   88.05 kg.
   D. 87.435 kg;   87.96 kg;   88.05 kg;   88.1 kg.

PROBLEM #16
Emily opened a hair salon in Eagle Pass. She kept track of the time
she spent cutting hair for each customer one day last week. Based on
Emily's information listed below, what would the "median" time be?
15 min; 25 min; 25 min; 20 min; 23 min; 30 min; 21 min; 27 min.
   A. 20 min.   B. 22 min.   C. 24 min.   D. 229 min.

PROBLEM #17
Terri is making tacos. It takes four pounds of hamburger to feed sixteen
people. How many pounds of hamburger would she need to feed eighty people?
   A. 100 pounds.   B. 68 pounds.   C. 64 pounds.   D. 20 pounds.

PROBLEM #18
After the Winter Ball; Nathan, Tiffany, Scott and Whitney went out
for dessert. Each person ordered a dessert which cost between $3.95 and
$5.25. Which of these is a good estimate of the total cost of the desserts
before tax?
   A. less than $10.   B. Between $8 and $10.
   C. Between $15 and $21.   D. More than $25.

WARMUPS
1. 31.3 – 5	4. $85.95	6. 9 1/6	8. 9½ ÷ 6
2. 31.3 – .5	× .8	– 7 3/5	9. 5^3
3. 31.3 – 50	5. 42 ÷ .00007	7. 5/8 × 48	10. $\sqrt{36}$

SOLVE THE FOLLOWING:
11.   15 / 25 = N / 100   **12.**   15 / A = 45 / 60   **13.** .005 / 12 = 30 / T

PROBLEM #14
Anglin Poultry Farm of Alvarado has 808 chickens. About 24% of the chickens lay an egg each day. Which would be the best estimate of the number of eggs laid each day at the Anglin Poultry Farm.
    A. 1600 eggs   B.   832 eggs   C.   200 eggs   D.   100 eggs

PROBLEM #15
Solena of San Angelo decorated the inside of her locker. She spent $4.95 for a mirror, $3.75 for a calendar, and $8.29 for a message board. How much change did she get back from a $20.00 bill?
    A. $ 3.00   B. $ 3.01   C. $16.99   D. $23.01

PROBLEM #16
Tom from Texas City Junction bought two dozen donuts for $7.78 (excluding tax). How much did each donut cost, to the nearest cent?
    A. $0.14   B. $0.32   C. $0.65   D. $3.38

PROBLEM #17
Jordan's parents always give him a lecture when he comes in late. He kept track of the length of each lecture last month. Based on the times listed below, what is the "mean" time of the lectures. LECTURE TIMES: 8 min;   12 min; 6 min;   10 min;   4 min;   6 min;   6 min;   4 min;
    A. 4 min.   B. 6 min.   C. 7 min.   D 5 min.

PROBLEM #18
A cube has 6 faces which are lettered from A to F. If the cube is rolled once, what is the probability that a vowel will be rolled?
    A. 1/6   B. 1/3   C. 1/2   D. 2/1

WARMUPS

1. 42.2 − 6	4. 54 ÷ .009	7. 13 − 8⅔	9. 7^3
2. 42.2 − 60	5. .8 ÷ 60	8. $75.55	10. $\sqrt{196}$
3. 42.2 − .06	6. 7 1/2 × 4/5	× .6	

SOLVE THE FOLLOWING:

11. 3R − 21 = 39   **12.** 8I + 2I = 30   **13.** 14 / 24 = 21 / C

PROBLEM #14

Last month, Berglund's Appliance Store in Big Sandy had a ratio of 5 to 3 of washing machines to dryers sold. If 48 dryers were sold, how many washing machines were sold?

   A. 80   B. 50   C. 28.8   D. 56

PROBLEM #15

The $\sqrt{54.2}$ is between which pair of consecutive integers?

   A. 27 and 28.   B. 6 and 7.   C. 7 and 8.   D. 8 and 9.

PROBLEM #16

There are six red golf tees, four white golf tees and ten blue golf tees in Mr. Maires' golf hat. If Nan draws out one golf tee, what is the probability that she will draw a white golf tee? red golf tee?

   A. 3/10; 1/2   B. 1/2; 3/10   C. 3/10; 1/5   D. 1/5;   3/10

PROBLEM #17

Mr. Hopper of Sugarland shot the following scores in March on Greatwood Golf Course: 84; 84; 91; 79; 83; 82; 82; 88; 82; What is Mr. Hopper's "MEDIAN" score for the month of March on Greatwood Golf Course?

   A. 82   B. 83   C. 84   D. 85

PROBLEM #18

Stine from Lyngby had the following meals on her expense account on her business trip to Atlanta. Sunday $18.25; Monday $24.80; Tuesday $31.65; Wednesday $21.75; Thursday $ 8.56; Friday $44.77; Saturday $28.02. Find: 1.The total Stine spent for meals. 2. Stine's "MEAN" meal expense per day.

   A. $168.70; $26.20   B. $168;70; $25.40
   C. $177.80; $26.20   D. $177.80; $25.40

LESSON #106   TEST PREPARATION

WARMUPS

1. $25.6 - 4$
2. $25.6 - .4$
3. $25.6 - 40$

4. $25.6 - .04$
5. $\begin{array}{r} \$56.00 \\ \times \quad .08 \\ \hline \end{array}$

6. $240 \div .008$
7. $\begin{array}{r} 7\ 1/2 \\ -\ 5\ 4/5 \\ \hline \end{array}$

8. $3/4 \div 2/3$
9. 4^3
10. $\sqrt{144}$

SOLVE THE FOLLOWING:

11. $24 / N = 60 / 35$ 12. $5T + 37 = 2T + 58$

13. What is the perimeter and area of a right triangle with legs of 9 and 12 inches and a hypotenuse of 15 inches?

PROBLEM #14

Tom, Eric, Rally, Mick, and Rachel are going to play in a one-on-one ping pong tournament. If each of them play one game against all the others, how many games will be played in all?

A. 4 games   B. 8 games   C. 10 games   D. 16 games

PROBLEM #15

Four students were asked to solve this problem:

$$6 + 4 \times 8 - 10(5 - 2) =$$

Shannon says the answer is 210. John says the answer is 50. Adrienne says the answer is 8 and Miriam says the answer is 68. Who is right?

A. Shannon   B. John   C. Adrienne   D. Miriam

PROBLEM #16

You are traveling from Longview through Kalama to Woodland. There are 4 routes from Longview to Kalama and 2 routes from Kalama to Woodland. How many different possible routes can you take from Longview to Woodland?

A. 4   B. 6   C. 8   D. 16

PROBLEM #17

There are 26 people in the math club; 11 boys and 15 girls. Four more people join the club. Out of the 30 people now in the math club, what can be said for certain about the fractional part of boys in the class? Do they make up less than ½, no more than ½, exactly ½. or at least ½ of the class?

A. Less than ½   B. No more than ½
C. Exactly ½   D. At least ½

PROBLEM #18

Kirsten's obese, lazy dog is awake one sixth of the whole day. It only wakes up when it hears the electric can opener opening its dog food. How many hours is Kristen's lazy dog awake and how many hours is it asleep?

A. Awake 6 hours; Asleep 18 hours.   B. Awake 18 hours; Asleep 6 hours.
C. Awake 4 hours; Asleep 20 hours.   D. Awake 20 hours; Asleep 4 hours.

1. 32.4 – 6   4. 32.4 + .45 + 3.16   7. ¾ × 1⅔   9. 6^3
2. 32.4 – .6   5. 24 ÷ .006   8.   8 ¼   10. $\sqrt{400}$
3. 32.4 – 60   6. .24 ÷ 60 $\underline{-5\ ⅓}$

SOLVE THE FOLLOWING:
11. 8C – 14 = 3C + 21   **12.** 14 = ?% of 35?
13. What is the perimeter and area of a right triangle with legs 5" and 12"
    and a hypotenuse of 13"?

PROBLEM #14
If you are told that the area of a square garden is 144 square feet, how
many feet of fence would it take to enclose the garden?
   A. 12 feet   C. 576   feet
   B. 48 feet   D. 20,736 feet

PROBLEM #15
Susan is saving to go on a cruise. The cruise costs $500.00. She
already has $263.00 in savings. Every week she earns $15 mowing lawns
and gets an $8 allowance. If Susan saves all the money she earns, how
many more weeks will it take her to earn enough money to pay for the cruise?

   A. 2 weeks   C. 11 weeks
   B. 8 weeks   D. 15 weeks

PROBLEM #16
Which expression should be next in this pattern?
5m + 4;   10m + 8;   20m + 16;   40m + 32;
   A. 8m + 48   C. 75m + 60
   B. 60m + 48   D. 80 m + 64

PROBLEM #17
Which expression is equivalent to 6(4w + 3y + 5)?
   A. 10w + 9y + 1   C. 24w + 3y + 5
   B. 24w + 18y + 30   D. 42wy + 30

PROBLEM #18
After receiving a scholarship offer from Florida State, Mark's hat size
increased. He wants to buy a new FSU fitted hat from Athlete's Corner.
The hat sells for $30, but fortunately Mark found that college hats were
30% off this week. How much money did Mark save on the hat and how
much did he owe Athlete's Corner?
   A. saved $9   owed $39   C. saved $21   owed $ 9
   B. saved $9   owed $21   D. saved $21   owed $51

LESSON #108   **TEST PREPARATION**
WARMUPS

1. 24.3 − 9   4. 24.32 − 90   6. 4 2/3 ÷ 7/9   8. 60% of $75.00
2. 24.3 − .9   5.   8   7. $75.00   9. 8^3
3. 24.32 + 9.8   − 7 3/5   ×   .6   10. $\sqrt{121}$

SOLVE THE FOLLOWING:
11. 24 / N = 60 / 75   **12.** 28 = ?% of 35?   **13.** 17C + 8C = 5C − 60

PROBLEM #14
Marcia sold 21 candy bars and Paula sold 32 candy bars. If a box holds 12 candy bars, how many boxes did Coach Selby have to open to fill these two girls' orders?
A. 4 Boxes   C. 6 Boxes
B. 5 Boxes   D. 7 Boxes

PROBLEM #15
Which expression should be next in the following pattern?
2T − 3;   6T − 9;   18T − 27;
   A. 27T − 36   C. 72T − 108
   B. 54T − 81   D. 36T − 54

PROBLEM #16
Which expression is equivalent to 7(9UC − 5L + A)?
A. 63UC − 35L + A   C. 7UC − 35L + 7A
B. 63UC − 35L + 7A   D. 105 UCLA

PROBLEM #17
Mr. Marcum bought a pass for 8 golf rounds at Bandon Dunes Golf Course. One round usually costs $120.00 at Bandon Dunes. Mr. Marcum paid $720.00 for his 8 round pass. How much money did Mr. Marcum save on his 8 round pass? What percent of the regular price did Mr. Marcum save?
A. $240.00 saved: 33⅓% saved. C. $240.00 saved: 25% saved.
B. $180.00 saved: 33⅓% saved. D. $180.00 saved: 25% saved.

PROBLEM #18
Given the following information, find a set of 11 numbers that fit the data below:
Range: 5 to 15,   Median: 8,   Mode 7,   Mean 9, and the average of the greatest two numbers is 14.
   A. 5, 7, 7, 7, 7, 8, 8, 10, 12, 13, 15.
   B. 5, 7, 7, 7, 7, 8, 8, 8, 10, 13, 15.
   C. 5, 7, 7, 7, 7, 8, 8, 10, 12, 14, 14.
   D. 5, 7, 7, 8, 8, 8, 8, 10, 12, 13, 15.

(108)

WARMUPS

1. $43.65 - 5.2$ 4. $4\frac{1}{2} \div 3$ 6. $\$63.28 \div 7$ 8. 40% of $75
2. $43.55 - .52$ 5. $\$63.28$ 7. $\begin{array}{r} 8 \\ -5\,4/5 \end{array}$ 9. 4^3
3. $43.65 - 52$ $\underline{\times \quad .07}$ 10. $\sqrt{81}$

SOLVE THE FOLLOWING:
11. $8 / T = 20 / 30$ **12.** $4M - 24 = 16$ **13.** $5N + 3N = 48$

PROBLEM #14
Lassette was sent to the store by her mother to buy a gallon of milk.
She can buy a quart of milk for $1.25 or a gallon for $4.25. How much
will she save by buying a gallon instead of 4 quarts?
  A. $0.25 B. $0.50 C. $0.75   D. $1.00

PROBLEM #15
Scott Selby will be playing tight end for the Washington State Cougars.
The team would like him to weigh 240 lbs. when he starts playing. If he
gains 5 lb. each month for 7 months, he will be at the desired weight. What
was his starting weight??
  A. 205 lbs B. 228 lbs.   C. 235 lbs   D. 275 lbs

PROBLEM #16
Marianne found her first part-time job working at Starbucks for $6.75
an hour. She works 20 hours per week, Starbucks withholds 15% of her pay
for federal income tax and 5% for state income tax. What will her net
income be if she is paid every two weeks?
  A. $135.00 B. $216.00 C. $270.00 D $324.00

PROBLEM #17
In college football, points can be scored as follows: touchdown 6 points;
extra point one point or two points; field goal 3 points; safety 2 points.
If the University of Texas Longhorns scored 40 points, which of these is a
possible way that they got this score?
  A. 5 touchdowns, three extra points and a field goal.
  B. 4 touchdowns, four extra points and three field goals.
  C. 6 touchdowns, a safety and a field goal.
  D. 3 touchdowns, three extra points, three field goals and
      three safeties.

PROBLEM #18
St. Rose School decided to put on a play for a fundraiser. Tickets for
the play cost $5.00. Two hundred forty people attended the play and one
half of the playgoers visited the concession stand where they spent $3.00
each. How much money did the school take in?
  A. $1,200.00 B. $1,560.00 C. $1,920.00 D. $3,600.00

LESSON #110   TEST PREPARATION

WARMUPS
1. 21.6 – 4
2. 21.6 – .4
3. 21.6 – 40
4. 21.6 + 4.44
5. ½ × ⅔
6. ½ ÷ ⅔
7. 9
   – 5 ¾
8. 46 ÷ .004
9. 11^2
10. $\sqrt{144}$

SOLVE THE FOLLOWING:
11. $8T + 31 = 71$ 12. $5T + 6T = T + 50$ 13. $15 / 9 = T / 3$

PROBLEM #14
Find the diagonal of a rectangle whose width is 12 cm and length is 5 cm.
  A. $\sqrt{17}$ cm   B. 7 cm   C. 13 cm   D. 17 cm

PROBLEM #15
The length and width of a rectangle have a ratio of three to two. If the perimeter of the rectangle is 170 cm, find the length and width.
  A. w = 20 cm; l= 30 cm   B. w = 34 cm; l = 51 cm
  C. w = 40 cm; l = 60 cm   D. w = 70 cm; l = 100 cm

PROBLEM #16
When Beth started her job at Shannon's Seafood Shack in Seabrook she made $6.40 an hour. She now makes $284.00 for a 40 hour week. How much more does Beth make an hour now than she made when she started?
  A. $.70   B. $.71   C. $7.00   D. $7.10

PROBLEM #17
On Thursday the Texas Rangers took in about $20,000 from box seat ticket sales. After the Rangers cut the price on the box seats, the attendance increased by 5,000 people in those seats. How much did the attendance change after The Texas Rangers dropped the price of the box seats?
A. Attendance increased by half.
B. Attendance doubled.
C. It is impossible to tell unless you know the new ticket price.
D. It is impossible to tell unless you know the original ticket price.

PROBLEM #18
Keisa had $22 to spend on rides at the Del Rio County Fair. The rides cost $4.00 and $5.00. Could Keisa spend exactly $22.00 for the rides?
  A. Yes.
  B. No, she would have $1.00 left over.
  C. No, she would have $2.00 left over.
  D. No, she would have $3.00 left over.

WARMUPS

1. $54.45 - 5$ 4. $54.45 + 55.55$ 6. $7/8 \div 3/4$ 9. $(⅓)^3$
2. $54.45 - .5$ 5. $4 ⅓$ 7. $60 \div .003$ 10. $\sqrt{81}$
3. $54.45 - 50$ $- 1 ¾$ 8. $.003 \div 60$

SOLVE THE FOLLOWING:

11. $6N + 4N = 2N + 24$ 12. $3N - 18 = 12$ 13. $8 / N = 36 / 45$

PROBLEM #14

Mr. Hopper from Sugarland has a rectangle forty-eight feet by twenty feet for his backyard. He drew a diagonal across this rectangle to make two right triangles. Mr. Hopper planted grass in one of the right triangles and low maintenance Texas bushes in the other right triangle. He then poured a thin line of concrete to separate the two right triangles. How long will this thin line of concrete be?

   A. 40 feet   B. 68 feet   C. 52 feet   D. 60 feet

PROBLEM #15

Zak from Mission Hills went on the Texas Ruby Red Diet. He lost four pounds a week for the first three weeks he was on the diet. He lost three pounds a week for the next two weeks he was on the diet and two pounds a week for the next three weeks. If Zak's weight right in the middle of his diet was 180 pounds, what was his starting and ending weights?

Starting weight	Ending Weight	Starting weight	Ending weight
A. 189 lbs	171 lbs	B. 195 lbs	165 lbs.
C. 195 lbs	171 lbs	D. 189 lbs	165 lbs

PROBLEM #16

Kami bought Texas burnt orange golf shirts for her two favorite teachers, Mr. **H** and Mr. **T.** She also bought one for her favorite principal, Mr. **M** and one for herself. Texas burnt orange golf shirts sell at three for $126.00. How much did Kami spend on Texas burnt orange golf shirts?

   A. $168.00   B. $167.50   C. $169.50   D. $156.00

PROBLEM #17

Lisa got a job at Stacia's Triangle Grill in Sabine last July. Lisa started at $6.60 an hour. After a month, Stacia gave Lisa a 20% raise. How much was Lisa making an hour after the raise?

   A. $7.70   B. $7.60   C. $8.25   D. $7.92

PROBLEM #18

Lisa (problem #17) worked 50 hours during the Lower Sabine Rodeo Days week last September. How much did she make during the Lower Sabine Rodeo Days week?

A. $396.00   B. $380.00

C. $385.00   D. You can't tell from the information given.

LESSON #112 MIXTURE
WARM UPS
1. $34.7 - 4$ 4. $\frac{3}{4} \times \frac{2}{3}$ 7. $.003 \div 60$ 9. 2^5
2. $34.7 - 40$ 5. $\frac{3}{4} \div \frac{2}{3}$ 8. 40% of $75.60?   10. $\sqrt{121}$
3. $34.7 - .4$ 6. $60 \div .003$

SOLVE THE FOLLOWING:
11. $84 / 60 = T / 45$ 12. $60 = 80\%$ of what number?
13. Find the perimeter and area of a 25ft. by 40ft. rectangle.

PROBLEM #14
Butch & Jerri drove Interstate 5 from Longview, Washington to Los Angeles, California. They drove the first 325 miles from Longview to Ashland, Oregon in five hours. If they drive at the same rate of speed the rest of the way, how long will it take them to drive to Los Angeles from Ashland? It is 1040 miles from Longview to Los Angeles. If Butch drove 665 of these miles, how many miles did Jerri drive?
A. 12 ½ hr; 375 mi. B. 12 hr; 365 mi. C.11 hr; 375 mi. D. 10 ½ hr; 365 mi.

PROBLEM #15
Butch and Jerri filled their gas tank six times on their Los Angeles trip. They paid: $1.93, $1.46, $1.72, $1.35, $1.51, and $1.41 per gallon of gas. What was the average price per gallon of gas that Butch and Jerri paid?
A. $1.56 per gal. B. $1.51 per gal. C. $1.48 per gal. D. $1.43 per gal.

PROBLEM #16
Mick and Earlene have a 40 ft. by 60 ft. rectangular back yard at their home in Del Rio. They want to plant "SUPER HUSKY DESERT CRAB GRASS" in one sixth of their back yard and leave the rest in natural desert sand and rocks. How many square feet of their back yard will be in "SUPER HUSKY DESERT CRAB GRASS"? How many square feet will be in natural desert sand and rocks?
Grass   A. 600 sq ft. B. 400 sq ft..   C. 800   sq. ft D.   300 sq. ft.
Sand & Rocks   1,800 sq. ft   2,000 sq. ft.   1,600   sq. ft.   2,100 sq. ft.

PROBLEM #17
Mick and Earlene (prob. 16) can buy "SUPER HUSKY DESERT CRAB GRASS" sod at $95.00 per 100 square feet. They want to put a Varmet Proof wire fence around the outside part of their back yard that does not border their house. This is four fifths of their back yard. Varmet Proof wire fence sells for $2.67 a foot. What will it cost Mick and Earlene for sod? What will it cost them for their fence?
A. $380.00 sod; $427.20 fence. B. $380.00 sod; $400.50 fence.
C. $570.00 sod; $422.20 fence. D. $570.00 sod; $400.50 fence

PROBLEM #18
Doug C. from East St. Louis bought a new miracle golf driver from Chris's General Golf Store in San Antonio. The driver normally sells for $360.00. Doug got the normal General Store's 20% discount plus another 15% discount for prefered customers.How much did Doug save on the driver? How much did Doug pay for the driver?
A. Doug saved $54.00; paid $306.00 B. Doug saved $72.00; paid $188.00
C. Doug saved $135.00; paid $225.00 D. Doug saved $126.00; paid $234.00

LESSON #113   MIXTURE

WARMUPS
1. 21.6 − 8
2. 21.6 − .8
3. 21.8 − 80
4. 4 1/3 × 6/13
5. 5/8 ÷ 1 1/3
6. 6 − 2¾
7. 20% of $95.25?
8. 12 ÷ .004
9. 10^5
10. $\sqrt{256}$

SOLVE THE FOLLOWING:
11. 60 / 24 = N / 60   12. Find the average of: 28, 42, 50, 27, and 33.
13. What is the perimeter and area of a rectangle 18ft. by 28ft.?

PROBLEM #14
Conrad of Corrigan paid $23,100 of his taxes. This was done by his withholding from his paycheck. However, this was only 55% of his taxes. What was Conrad's total tax bill?
  A. $46,200   B. $31,500   C. $40,000   D. $42,000

PROBLEM #15
Five out of every seven red snapper and sea bass caught by Steve Carter of Grove are legal size. The rest have to be thrown back. Last April, Steve threw back 27 red snapper and 15 sea bass. How many total fish did Steve catch in April? How many were legal size?
  A. 147 fish caught; 90 legal size.   B. 147 fish caught; 105 legal size.
  C. 189 fish caught:; 147 legal size   D. 55 fish caught; 13 legal size.

PROBLEM #16
Lath from Fresno bought two dozen Texas Ruby Red grapefruit at Squeak's Fruit Stand. Squeak sells Texas Ruby Red grapefruit three for $.87. How much did Lath pay for the grapefruit?
  A. $ 3.48   B. $8.71   C. $7.24   D. $6.96

PROBLEM #17
The Houston Astros won eleven games in April, eleven in May, eight in June, fourteen in July, seventeen in August, and eleven in September. How many total wins did the Houston Astros have? How many wins did they average per month?
  A. 72 wins; 12 per month.   B. 72 wins; 10 per month.
  C. 68 wins; 12 per month.   D. 68 wins; 10 per month.

PROBLEM #18
Traci from Rancho Cucamonga has walls in her bedroom that are all rectangles. They are 12 ft. by 8 ft., 16 ft. by 8 ft., 12 ft.by 8 ft., and 16 ft. by 8 ft.. Traci has a 3 ft. by 7 ft. door and a 4 ft. by 2½ ft. window she does not want to paint. About how many square feet does Traci need to buy paint for in order to paint her walls?
  A. 389 sq. ft.   B. 448 sq. ft.   C. 479 sq. ft.   D. 417 sq. ft

LESSON #114   MIXTURE
WARMUPS
1. 41.4 – 6   4. 14 + -41 – (-27)   7. .04 ÷ 800   9. $(-3)^4$
2. 41.4 – 60   5. ¾ × 48   8. 25% of $48   10. $\sqrt{169}$
3. -8 × 5 ÷ -2   6. 5 1/3 ÷ 4/9

SOLVE THE FOLLOWING:
11. 40 / 24 = 30 / T   12. 24 / I = 75 / 100   13. 9M + 7M = 6M + 70

PROBLEM #14
The Thompsons of Rosedale made $300 at their garage sale. They split the money this way: Shaun 3/5; Sydni 1/4; and Ginger the rest. How much money did each Thompson make on the garage sale?
A. Shaun $180; Sydni $75; Ginger $45. B. Shaun $120; Sydni $75; Ginger $105.
C. Shaun $180; Sydni $90; Ginger $30. D. Shaun $120; Sydni $9;   Ginger $90.

PROBLEM #15
The Pattersons of McCormick Woods hit 90 practice golf balls on the driving range. Ben hit ⅓ of the balls. Sherri hit 20% of the balls. Hanna hit one tenth of the balls and Al hit the rest. How many golf balls did each Patterson hit on the driving range?
A. Ben 25; Sherri 18; Hanna 9; Al 38. B. Ben 30; Sherri 18; Hanna 9; Al 33.
C. Ben 30; Sherri 16; Hanna 9; Al 35. D. Ben 25; Sherri 16; Hanna 9; Al 40.

PROBLEM #16
Tim and Kathy drove the 120 miles from Longview to Gig Harbor on Saturday. They drove home to Longview on Sunday from Gig Harbor. Tim drove 1/3 of the miles on Saturday and 4/5 of the miles on Sunday. Kathy drove the rest of the miles. How many miles did Tim drive? How many miles did Kathy drive?
A. 144; 96.   B. 120; 120.   C. 150; 90.   D. 136; 104.

PROBLEM #17
The co-operative part of the Gig Harbor High School Math Department put together a real useful book on **Math Lessons And Techniques.** Jim, the leader, did one fifth of the pages. Ginger, the most enthusiastic in the math department, did one third of the pages. Sherri reluctantly did 25% of the pages. Robin did 10% and Pete did the rest. If the **Math Lessons And Techniques** book contained 60 pages, how many pages did each member of the math department contribute?

	Jim	Ginger	Sherri	Robin	Pete
A.	15;	18;	18;	6;	3
B.	15;	20;	18;	6;	1
C.	12;	20;	15;	6;	7
D.	12;	18;	15;	6;	9

PROBLEM #18
Ted, Al, Dick, and Gavin caught eleven fish the first day of their five day fishing trip to Alaska. Ted caught twice as many fish as Al and one more fish than Gavin. Dick caught the same number of fish as Al. If they each catch the same number of fish on each of the other four days of their trip, how many fish will the foursome catch all together? How many total fish will Al catch? How many fish will Gavin catch?
A. 55 total fish; Al 15; Gavin 20.   B. 55 total fish; Al 10; Gavin 15.
C. 44 total fish; Al 8; Gavin 12.   D. 44 total fish; Al 12; Gavin 16.

LESSON #115   MIXTURE

WARMUPS
1. 35.5 – 6
2. 35.5 – 60
3. 35.5 – .6
4. $35.50 + $6 – $17.75
5. 8 – 3 3/4
6. 5 1/2 ÷ 11/12
7. 40% of $70?
8. 2/5 of $70?
9. 4^4
10. $\sqrt{121}$

SOLVE THE FOLLOWING
11. $9T - 36 = 27$ 12. $24 / T = 36 / 42$ 13. 75% of ? = 42

PROBLEM #14
Dae from Cathlamet makes 25% profit on all the lunch meat he sells at his Highway Market. If Roy bought $54 worth of bologna and $52 worth of turkey, how much profit will Dae make from these sales?
A. $28.00 B. $26.50   C. $24.75 D. $40.00

PROBLEM #15
Jin from Juarez drove three-fifths of the way from Juarez to Phoenix. Mary drove the rest of the way. If it is 435 miles from Juarez to Phoenix, how many miles did Jin drive? How many miles did Mary drive?
A. Jin 240 miles; Mary 195 miles.   B. Jin 348 miles; Mary 87 miles.
C. Jin 250 miles; Mary 185 miles.   D. Jin 261 miles; Mary 174 miles.

PROBLEM #16
Michael from Ostrander drives 5¼ miles to work. Michael worked 25 days last August, 26 days last September and 21 days last October. How many miles did Michael drive to and from work during these three months last year?
A. 756 miles B. 792 miles. C. 378 miles. D. 720 miles.

PROBLEM #17
Mr. Joos from Jacinto City works four days on and then has four days off. His work schedule is always the same; four on, four off. Mr. Joos worked August 1st. If this was the 3rd day of his four days at work, how many days did he work in August?
A. 13 B. 14   C. 15   D. 16

PROBLEM #18
Twenty-four percent of the Tuesday Fibre Golf League are really not employees at Fibre, but are "Pseudo Fibre Leaguers". If there are six of these "Pseudo Fibre League" golfers, how many total Fibre League golfers are there? How many of these golfers actually work at Fibre?
A. 30 total; 24 work at Fibre. B. 20 total; 14 work at Fibre.
C. 25 total; 19 work at Fibre. D. 40 total; 34 work at Fibre.

LESSON #116   MIXTURE

WARMUPS
1. 75.24 − 9
2. 75.24 − 90
3. 75.24 − .9
4. 1/2 of $38.00
5. 1/2 of $39.00
6. 25% of $38.00
7. 3 1/2 × 4/7
8. 9 − 5 1/4
9. 2^5
10. $\sqrt{144}$

SOLVE THE FOLLOWING
11. 7Y + 22 = 57 **12.** 8 / 14 = **Y** / 35 **13.** What is the perimeter and area of a right triangle with legs of 14 inches and 48 inches and a hypotenuse of 50 inches?

During August, Yang, from Ace Distributors of Mt. Solo, drank four more cans of soda than Ki from Kalama. Gina from Galveston visited Yang for the month of August and drank four less than twice as many cans of soda as Ki. Dave from Grumbois drank ¼ as many cans of soda in August as Gina. Clay from Barti drank ⅔ as many cans of soda in August as Ki. If Yang and Ki together drank 40 total cans of soda in August, find the number of cans of soda drank by:

PROBLEM #14 Yang?
   A. 18   B. 22   C. 20   D. 24

PROBLEM #15 Ki?
   A. 18   B. 22   C. 20   D. 24

PROBLEM #16 Gina?
   A. 40   B. 28   C. 36   D. 32

PROBLEM #17 Dave?
   A. 12   B. 10   C. 6   D. 8

PROBLEM #18 Clay?
   A. 12   B. 10   C. 4   D. 8

LESSON #117   MIXTURE

WARMUPS
1. $27.30 − $5
2. $27 − $5.30
3. $27.30 + $8 + $4.70
4. .04 ÷ 50
5. 2/3 × $36
6. 4 1/5 ÷ 3/4
7. $70.65
$\times$ .8
8. 80% of $70.65
9. 10^5
10. $\sqrt{121}$

SOLVE THE FOLLOWING:
11. 24 is 80% of ?   **12.** 18 / **T** = 45 / 35   **13.** 9T = 2T + 42

PROBLEM #14   Tanner from Johnsonville has 54 total sports cards in his collection. About 43% of these cards are football cards. Close to thirty percent of his cards are baseball. The rest are basketball. Approximately how many football, basketball and baseball cards does Tanner have?

	A	B	C	D
Football	24	24	23	23
Basketball	14	16	16	15
Baseball	16	14	15	15

PROBLEM #15
   Last summer, Tyler of Scottsbluff hit 32 drives past the trapezoid on the 4th hole at the Longview Country Club. If this was 80% of Tyler's drives on hole 4, how many total drives did Tyler hit on hole #4 last summer? How many were not past the trapezoid?
  A. 25 total; 7 not   B. 50 total; 18 not   C. 36 total; 4 not   D. 40 total; 8 not

PROBLEM #16
   Aaron from Castle Rock left home and drove the 1 hour ten minute drive to the Portland Airport. He had a 52 minute wait for his flight to Boston and a five hour fifty-four minute flight. If Aaron left Castle Rock at 4:30 PM, what time did he land in Boston?
  A. 3:26 AM   B. 4:56 AM C. 2:26 AM   D. 3:56 AM

PROBLEM #17
   Seven out of every nine students in Miss Franett's 1st period math class have all their assignments turned in. If 8 students do not have all their assignments turned in, how many students have all their assignments turned in?
  A. 36   B. 24   C. 28   D. 30

PROBLEM #18
   Craig from Michigan paid $240.00 for an "Official Wolverine Football Fan Victory Outfit". Craig got a 25% discount at "The Big Ten Store" in Detroit. What was the original price of Craig's Wolverine Outfit? How much did Craig save at "The Big Ten Store"?
  A. $360; $120   B. $320; $80   C. $180; $60   D. $300; $60

LESSON #118   MIXTURE
WARMUPS
1. 52.09 − 7   4. .0036 ÷ 8   7. 20% of $35   9. 10^3
2. 52.09 − .7   5. ½ ÷ ¾   8. $81.18   10. $\sqrt{625}$
3. 52.09 − 70   6. 8 − 5 5/8   ×   .07

SOLVE THE FOLLWING:
11. A + 24 = 17   **12.** 3B = B + 12   **13.** 20 / 18 = **L** / 27

PROBLEM #14
Cindy from Carrols Bluff bought a power washer on sale at Longman's Hardware Store in Kalama. The power washer normally sells for $124.50. Cindy got a 20% discount at Longmans. How much did Cindy save on the power washer? How much did she pay for it?
  A. $12.45 saved; $112.05 paid   B. $31.13 saved; $93.37 paid
  C. $21.25 saved; $103.25 paid D. $24.90 saved; $99.60 paid

PROBLEM #15
Hanna from Gig Harbor got 57 points on Mrs. Patterson's math test. If this was 95% correct, how many points were on the test? How many points did Hanna miss?
  A. 65 points;   8 missed   B. 60 points; 3 missed
  C. 70 points; 13 missed   D. 62 points; 5 missed

PROBLEM #16
Al from Silverdale usually hits five out of every six golf drives in the fairway. Last March, Al hit his drive in the fairway 150 times. How many chances did Al have last March to hit his drive in the fairway? How many drives did Al miss the fairway?
  A. 200 chances; missed 50 times   B. 175 chances;   missed 25 times
  C. 170 chances; missed 20 times   D. 180 chances;   missed 30 times

PROBLEM #17
Tony of Escondido drove for 45 minutes to get to the San Diego Airport. He had a 47 minute wait at the airport for his flight. Tony flew to Orlando which is a 5 hr. 19 minute flight. If Tony left Escondido at 4:30 AM, what time did he land in Orlando?
  A. 2:21 PM   B. 2:02 PM   C. 1:02 PM   D. 12:21 PM

PROBLEM #18
The Men's NCAA Basketball Tournament starts with 64 teams. The winners keep playing and the losers go home. One half of the 64 teams played Thursday, March 18th. The teams that won played again on Saturday, March 20th. The other half of the 64 teams played on Friday, March 19th, and the winners played again on Sunday, March 21st. On Saturday night, March 20th; after all Saturday's games were finished, how many teams were still in the Tournament?
  A. 32   B. 24   C. 20   D. 16

LESSON #119   MIXTURE

WARMUPS
1. $45.54 - 9$
2. $45.54 - 90$
3. $45.54 - .9$

4. 60% of \$75?
5. $7\frac{1}{2} \times 14$
6. $15 - 4\,5/6$

7. $\begin{array}{r}\$75.50 \\ \times\quad .06 \\ \hline\end{array}$
8. $7\frac{1}{3} - 5\frac{3}{4}$

9. $(.2)^5$
10. $\sqrt{.09}$

SOLVE THE FOLLOWING
11. $6 / 9 = 15 / T$ **12.** $.8 / I = 4 / .6$ **13.** Find the volume of a square prism whose edges are 8 in. each.

PROBLEM #14
Patty had 5 hogs she took to the county fair. There were named: Eddie, Tommy, Jimmy, Jeremy and Trenton. They averaged 542 lbs.. What did the five hogs weigh in all?
   A. 2,710 lbs.   B. 2,172 lbs.   C. 2,810 lbs.   D. 2,760 lbs.

PROBLEM #15
Eddie weighed 612 lbs. and Tommy weighed 504 lbs. How much did the other three hogs weigh?
   A. 1,694 lbs.   B. 4,304 lbs.   C. 1,594 lbs.   D. 1,696 lbs.

PROBLEM #16
If Eddie sold for \$.48 a pound, how much money was he sold for?
   A. \$1,275.00   B. \$127.50   C. \$2,937.60   D. \$293.76

PROBLEM #17
If Eddie and Tommy both sold for \$.38 a pound, how much more did Eddie sell for than Tommy?
   A. \$44.84   B. \$284.22
   C. \$41.04   D. None, Tommy sold for more!

PROBLEM #18
Trenton weighed 476 and Jeremy weighed 504. Which one of the five hogs weighed the most?
   A. Jeremy   B. Eddie   C. Tommy   D. Jimmy

LESSON #120   MIXTURE

WARMUPS

1. 13.2 − 4   4. $60 ÷ .005   7. $80.08   9. 3^4
2. 13.2 − 40   5. 9 1/2 × 4/9   ×   .11   10. $\sqrt{400}$
3. 13.2 − .4   6. 25% of $44   8. 20 − 12⅔

SOLVE THE FOLLOWING

11. 8 / T = 12 / 9   **12.** 5I − 13 = 17   **13.** What is the area and perimeter of a right triangle with legs of 5 and 12 inches and a hypotenuse of 13 inches?

PROBLEM #14

Megan of St. Helens got five more points on her math test than Alina of Scappoose. Alina got three points more than Dana from Deer Island. If three times Megan's score increased by nine points equals three hundred, find all three students scores.

	A.	B.	C.	D.
Megan	100	90	94	97
Alina	95	85	89	92
Dana	92	82	86	89

PROBLEM #15

Laurel of Porterville bought two stitching projects from Mannen's Craft Store in Goble. One stitching project cost three times as much as the other one. If Laurel spent a total of $60, how much was each project?
    A. $20, $80   B. $45, $15   C. $20, $40   D. $30, $30

PROBLEM #16

Dan from the St. Helens suburbs flies 35% of the time on United Airlines, 45% of the time on Alaska Airlines, and 20% of the time on Southwest Airlines. If he flew 8,000 miles on Southwest Airlines, how many miles did he fly on United Airlines? Alaska Airlines?

	A.	B.	C.	D.
United	14,000	3,600	28,000	18,000
Alaska	18,000	2,800	36,000	14,000

PROBLEM #17

Catherine S. from Philadelphia wanted to visit Longview, Washington, home of lots of clever and witty math word problems. It took Catherine 1 hr. 15 min. to drive to the Philadelphia Airport where she had a 52 min. wait for her flight. She flew 3hr. 20 min. to Denver, where she had a 1 hr. 25 min. layover. Her flight to Portland from Denver was 1 hr. 47 min.. It took Catherine 45 minutes to get her luggage, rent a car and another 53 minutes to drive from Portland to Longview. If Catherine left her home in Philadelphia at 6:30 AM, what time did she get to Longview, Washington?
    A. 4:47 PM   B. 7:47 PM   C. 1:47 PM   D. 4:13 PM

PROBLEM #18

Using the information in Problem #17, how much more time did Catherine S. from Philadelphia spend in the air than her non-flying time?
    A. 17 minutes   B. 1 hr. 17 minutes   C. 3 hr. 17 minutes   D. Actually her flying time was three minutes less than non-flying time.

(**120**)

LOOK AT THE TOPICS IN PRACTICE PRACTICE PRACTICE BOOK I+ AND BOOK II+.

PRACTICE PRACTICE PRACTICE BOOK I+

Whole numbers	Money
Basic Facts	Fractions
Decimals	Prime Numbers
Rounding	GCF & LCM
Comparing	Proportions
Percents	Word Problems

Plus over 25 review and combination pages!!!

PRACTICE PRACTICE PRACTICE BOOK II+

Proportions	Percents
Integers	Rationals
Equations	Inequalities
Scientific Notation	Estimation
Evaluating Expressions	Perimeter
Order of Operations	Area
Probability	Volume
Geometry	Word Problems

Plus 41 review & combination pages on the above topics
along with whole numbers, decimals, fractions & rounding.

If you had a copies of both Practice Practice Practice books on your desk, you would have over 20,000 organized, quality problems at your fingertips. Just think of the time this will save you!!!!!!

THE CLASSROOM SET IDEA

If you have a classroom set of Practice Practice Practice books in your room, it takes very little to supplement your daily lessons. The students can do the number of problems the classroom teacher assigns (one, three, seven, ten, etc) out of the Practice books, grade the problems, then put the book back for the next class. The students can now do the rest of the assignment out of their own text. You have provided extra practice with very little teacher preparation time.

Besides the time it saves the classroom teacher, a classroom set will cut the duplication costs of your math department. Some places claim to have saved enough in duplication costs in a year to pay for a classroom set.

If you have questions, please call, fax, email, or check our web site.

ST^2 PUBLISHING
191 Inglewood Dr.
Longview, WA 98632
TEL.   360-636-2645
FAX   360-414-5243

EMAIL - st2pub@kalama.com
WEB SITE -   st2pub.com